Joshua Tree National Park
GEOLOGY

D.D. TRENT, PROFESSOR EMERITUS,
DEPARTMENT OF GEOLOGY, CITRUS COLLEGE

RICHARD W. HAZLETT, ASSOCIATE PROFESSOR,
DEPARTMENT OF GEOLOGY, POMONA COLLEGE

JOSHUA TREE NATIONAL PARK ASSOCIATION

Copyright 2002 Joshua Tree National Park Association
74485 National Park Drive
Twentynine Palms, CA 92277
www.joshuatree.org

Joshua Tree National Park Association is a not-for-profit organization formed to assist with preservation, education, historical, and scientific programs for the benefit of Joshua Tree National Park and its visitors.

ISBN 0-9679756-1-1
Library of Congress Card Catalog Number 2002111924
First Edition

Edited by Sandra Scott
Design and Production by Christina Watkins and Amanda Summers
Illustrations by Susan Daigle-Leach
Printed in Singapore
Photography Credits:
    Gail Bandini — back cover & page 10
    Zandria Muench Beraldo — page 6
    George H. H. Huey — cover
    David Muench — page 4 & 38
    John S. Shelton — page 44
    Walter Stephens — page 42 (left)
    Larry Ulrich — cover inset & title page
    All other photographs courtesy D. D. Trent

CONTENTS

The Meaning of Joshua Tree National Park

*N*ational parks are the best idea
we ever had. Absolutely American,
absolutely democratic, they
reflect us at our best rather than
at our worst.

— WALLACE STEGNER

The national park concept goes back to about the time of the American Civil War, when President Abraham Lincoln designated Yosemite Valley a reserve in order to protect its beauty and recreational potential. A few years later the United States Congress established Yellowstone National Park, the world's first such designated land area. These early parks were managed and patrolled by the U.S. Army. A uniformed ranger service did not come into existence until 1916, when President Woodrow Wilson authorized establishment of the National Park Service within the Department of the Interior. In time, the American park system inspired comparable conservation efforts worldwide.

Why people thought it important to establish such an agency in the first place is a fascinating question. The answer is complex and one of the reasons that we write this short book. After all, our country's areas of great beauty and historical or scientific interest could all have been left open for commercial exploitation or private development.

The middle nineteenth and early twentieth centuries in America were times of rapid economic expansion coupled with high idealism and an almost romantic view of the world. The roots of this romanticism, which very much included an idyllic view of nature, go back to Europe, where the "purity" of classical Rome and Greece, of the "noble savage," and of pastoral life were all celebrated in the struggles to reform monarchies and democratize culture. In American literature and philosophy, we see strains of romantic naturalism in Henry David Thoreau, Herman Melville, John Muir, and Theodore Roosevelt, the president who is most closely associated with the conservation movement. Natural beauty is important and comforting to people. It is hard to say why. For a Thoreau it is because nature is a neutral healing ground, beyond the "quiet desperation" of ordinary urban life to which most of us are tied. It is a balm for the wounded or harried soul. To a Roosevelt, it is an environment in which people can challenge themselves, be it through the physical rigors of rock scrambling and backpacking or ordinary bird watching. Such challenges, in Roosevelt's opinion, help keep human beings whole, vital, and healthy.

A sense of history, too, is important. For example, the cliff dwellings at Mesa Verde and the battlefield at Gettysburg are protected as part of our national heritage.

Even though Mesa Verde served the needs of a people remote from today, and Gettysburg sadly commemorates the slaughter of tens of thousands of young men, preservation of such places and events helps us develop a sense of place in time and a better understanding of who we are. We encounter our roots by visiting these looking glasses to the past. In protecting natural beauty for the sake of the soul and protecting the past for the sake of understanding our place in the scheme of things, the National Park Service reflects our civic farsightedness.

It is to understand better who we are that motivated our writing this book. Geology, after all, is but an extension of history. (Or is it the other way around?) In a world imperiled by environmental problems, where the present calendars of humanity are so out of pace with the time lines of nature, it is all the more important that our sense of place encompass many millions, not merely hundreds, of years. Is this possible? We believe so and hope that you agree after you've finished these pages.

For those many harried souls who desire a brief escape from an increasingly congested urban world, the park's landscapes provide the healing role of nature that Thoreau described. If ever we decide our national parks are no longer needed, we will have lost something vital.

Joshua Tree — A Look at the Very Distant Past

The geological makeup of southern California in general is wonderfully and richly complex, and it is arguable that nowhere is this better reflected than in Joshua Tree National Park. The amazing rock formations of Joshua Tree enable us to look deep into Earth's past and comprehend the natural architecture of our continent's crust. While other parts of southern California have become paved over or made difficult to reach, we can still learn, on a grand scale, about climate change and the origins of land-scapes here; important topics for public understanding if we are ever to become better stewards of the earth.

The fantastic and wonderful adaptations of desert life, too, provide inspiration and ecological insights. A spontaneous and unique interaction of life, land, and climate

Deserts comprise an important part of the earth's landscape, and cover about 20 percent of the land surface.

is beautifully displayed here because the national park allows nature to run its course with minimal interference from human activity. The park encompasses and protects a valuable learning and recreational resource and, in some respects, is far richer and more meaningful an environment for new understanding than any university laboratory.

TODAY'S JOSHUA TREE

Joshua Tree National Park is in the desert, located near the center of southern California at the eastern end of a long, narrow, east–west trending mountain belt called the Transverse Ranges.

"Desert" means different things to different people. For some, a desert seems to be stark, barren regions of sand dunes; for others, it is a desolate region of bare, rocky outcrops and cactus. For many, it is a treasure trove of scenic wonders and unique plants and animals. The Romans, in their conquest of North Africa called its dry interior *desertus,* meaning barren or deserted. Our modern word is derived from the Latin. As it turns out, deserts are hardly deserted, and to the creatures living there, they are hardly barren.

No single geologic process is at work in a typical desert. Rather, the effects of running water, tectonic forces, and the wind are all apparent. Because these factors combine in different ways in different places, the appearance of desert landscapes varies as well.

WHAT IS A DESERT?

A DESERT MAY BEST BE DEFINED AS A REGION OF LOW RAINFALL AND HIGH EVAPORATION THAT IS CHARACTERIZED BY SCANTY VEGETATION AND DISTINCTIVE LANDFORMS. AN AUSTRALIAN EXPLORER OF A CENTURY AGO, WHO WAS SOMETHING OF A WAG, DEFINED DESERTS MORE SIMPLY AS "ANY BARREN TRACT OF LAND THAT IS TRULY DANGEROUS TO CROSS WITH CAMELS."

RAIN SHADOWS & HAWAIIAN HIGHS

There are two reasons that eastern California is a desert. One is a persistent fair-weather condition called the Hawaiian High, and the other is the rain shadow effect.

During the winter months, the Hawaiian High usually dissipates. Winter storms originating over the Pacific can pass in succession across the California desert, bringing rain and even snow. Of course, the coastal areas of California get the major share of this moisture, but enough precipitation may reach the desert to nurture spectacular spring flower displays and the grasses that turn the desert green for weeks.

Rainfall is not restricted to winter weather systems. During the late summer and fall, the Hawaiian High again weakens and moist air slips into the region across Arizona from the Gulf of Mexico bringing thunderstorms to the desert at a time when the days are still long and hot. Curiously, July and August are the months of greatest rainfall in the Joshua Tree region. Unlike the steady rains that drizzle down during winter storms, these thundershowers

THE CURIOUS TRANSVERSE RANGES

THIS MOUNTAIN SYSTEM RISES FROM THE PACIFIC OCEAN NEAR POINT ARGUELLO, 50 MILES (80 KM) WEST OF SANTA BARBARA, AND EXTENDS EASTWARD FOR NEARLY 300 MILES (500 KM). IT FORMS THE NORTHERN FRINGE OF THE LOS ANGELES METROPOLITAN AREA AND PASSES FAR INTO THE DESERT NORTH OF PALM SPRINGS AND INDIO. ITS EASTERN TERMINUS IS THE EAGLE MOUNTAINS, AT THE SOUTHEASTERN END OF JOSHUA TREE NATIONAL PARK. EAST-WEST TRENDING MOUNTAIN SYSTEMS SUCH AS THE TRANSVERSE RANGES ARE GEOGRAPHICAL ODDITIES IN NORTH AMERICA. MOST

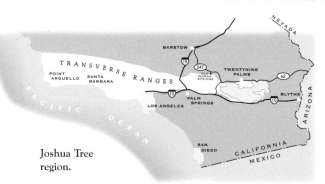

Joshua Tree region.

MOUNTAINS IN NORTH AMERICA TREND MORE NORTH-SOUTH. EXCEPTIONS SUCH AS THE TRANSVERSE RANGES ATTRACT THE ATTENTION OF GEOLOGISTS. SOMETHING UNUSUAL AND INTERESTING MUST ACCOUNT FOR THEM. THE LANDSCAPE OF JOSHUA TREE NATIONAL PARK PROVIDES CLUES TO THE ORIGINS OF THIS UNUSUAL LANDFORM.

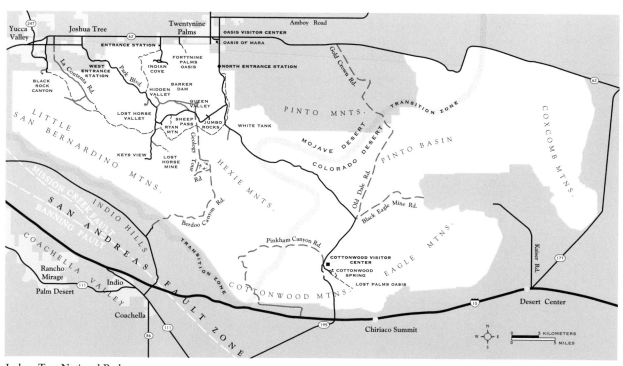

Joshua Tree National Park.

The Hawaiian High is a semi-permanent high-pressure air mass that forms in the atmosphere over the northeastern Pacific Ocean. It blocks the passage of moist weather systems over California, sometimes for months on end.

may trigger flash floods that wash countless tons of sediment through desert stream beds that are dry during the rest of the year. While most of California is parched during late summer, it is often raining from place to place in the state's south-eastern desert.

The average rainfall at Twentynine Palms is only a little over four inches (10 cm) but higher elevations within the park receive greater rainfall. One can travel from the low, dry eastern end of the park to the higher mountains of the west and see a transition in vegetation types from arid desert scrub land speckled with spindly ocotillo and cactus to pinyon-juniper forest. Such a dramatic change in vegetation represents not only a change in elevation, but also the effects of a closer proximity to the Pacific Ocean. For the ecologist as well as the geologist, Joshua Tree is a wonderland.

JOSHUA TREE'S CLIMATE

JOSHUA TREE NATIONAL PARK HAS A MID-LATITUDE ARID CLIMATE, MEANING THAT TEMPERATURES IN THE PARK, WHILE SOMETIMES SCORCHING DURING SUMMER MONTHS, ARE ACTUALLY RELATIVELY MODERATE DURING THE REST OF THE YEAR. WINTERS ARE COLD, WHILE THE AUTUMN AND SPRING ARE FULL OF PLEASANT DAYS, SOME QUITE COOL. THE AVERAGE ANNUAL TEMPERATURE AT TWENTYNINE PALMS, ELEVATION 2,000 FEET (610 M), FOR EXAMPLE, IS ONLY 67.3°F (19.5°C), AND AT HIDDEN VALLEY CAMPGROUND, ELEVATION 4,200 FEET (1,280 M), ABOUT 62°F (17°C).

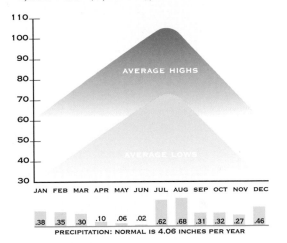

Average monthly rainfall and temperatures at Joshua Tree National Park, taken at 1,960 feet (598 m) elevation.

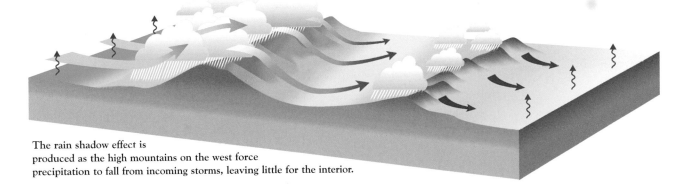

The rain shadow effect is produced as the high mountains on the west force precipitation to fall from incoming storms, leaving little for the interior.

Continental Shuffle — Back to the Basics

The story of the origin of the bedrock of the Joshua Tree landscape is also the story of how continents grow. The idea that continents grow larger with time goes back to the late eighteenth century and the earliest studies of geology, when James Hutton sketched and described ancient sea bed rocks that had been uplifted to form stable land in his native Scotland. However, just how continents grew bigger remained a mystery until the 1960s when deep-sea drilling led

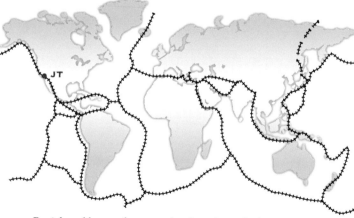

Partial world map of current plate boundaries. Joshua Tree lies astride the boundary separating the Pacific and North American Plates (dot). The San Andreas Fault marks this boundary in southern California.

researchers to understand that the earth's crust, bearing both the continents and ocean basins, is divided into lithospheric plates that move.

According to this theory of plate tectonics, restless but slow-moving currents of circulating hot rock inside the earth's mantle break up our planet's rigid outer rind, a layer termed the lithosphere (atop which we live), into huge curved slabs, called plates. The plates range in size from merely hundreds to thousands of miles across. Where the slow-moving currents upwell, plates may split and slide apart, creating ocean basins with narrow ridges of sea-floor volcanic vents, such as the Mid–Atlantic Ridge and the East Pacific Rise.

Elsewhere, one plate slides under another (subducts) to create dramatic mountain chains, such as the Alps and the Andes, many of which are also volcanically active. In other places, plates only scrape past one another, forming long, dangerously active fault lines like California's San Andreas Fault and Turkey's Anatolian Fault. It is collision and side scraping that most closely relate to the long history of Joshua Tree's spectacular landscape.

Growth of continents is a by-product of plate collision. The coast of a continent is a dumping ground of soft sediment carried from the continental interior to the sea by rivers and streams. This sediment accumulates to vast thicknesses, forming a continental shelf. The tiny pore spaces between the countless particles of sediment fill with

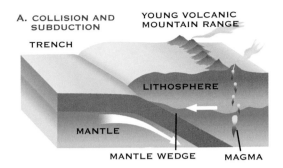

A. COLLISION AND SUBDUCTION

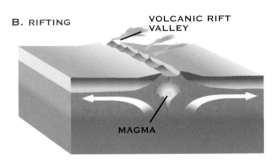

B. RIFTING

C. COLLISION AND SIDEWAYS SCRAPING

Three basic kinds of motion may occur at plate boundaries. A. subduction; B. pulling apart (rifting); and C. sideways (lateral) faulting.

water that is laden with dissolved chemicals. These chemicals precipitate cements that bind the soft sediments together, eventually to form coherent sedimentary rocks like sandstone and siltstone.

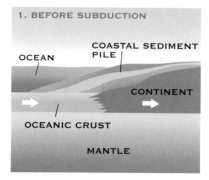

1. BEFORE SUBDUCTION

OCEAN

COASTAL SEDIMENT PILE

CONTINENT

OCEANIC CRUST

MANTLE

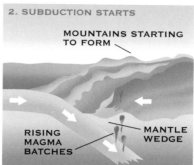

2. SUBDUCTION STARTS

MOUNTAINS STARTING TO FORM

RISING MAGMA BATCHES

MANTLE WEDGE

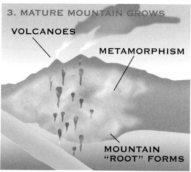

3. MATURE MOUNTAIN GROWS

VOLCANOES

METAMORPHISM

MOUNTAIN "ROOT" FORMS

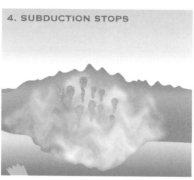

4. SUBDUCTION STOPS

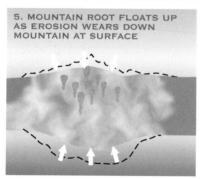

5. MOUNTAIN ROOT FLOATS UP AS EROSION WEARS DOWN MOUNTAIN AT SURFACE

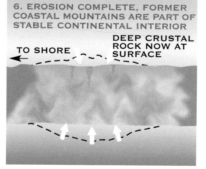

6. EROSION COMPLETE, FORMER COASTAL MOUNTAINS ARE PART OF STABLE CONTINENTAL INTERIOR

TO SHORE

DEEP CRUSTAL ROCK NOW AT SURFACE

From coastal mud to hard continential rock.

MOUNTAIN BUILDING AND ROCK MELTING

When the earth's deep, hot, rock circulates in such a way as to drag the coastal regions of a continent into collision with the neighboring lithospheric plate, the offshore shelf sediments caught in the squeeze between the colliding plates crumple and rise out of the sea, giving birth to a new coastal mountain range.

The sedimentary materials are heated during the collision and their minerals are transformed into new, strongly interlocking mineral crystals. This process is called metamorphism. When associated with mountain building, metamorphism converts weak sedimentary rocks into durable rocks that become permanently welded to the continent.

There are many kinds of metamorphic rocks. Marble and quartzite, for example, form by the metamorphism of limestone and sandstone, respectively, two very common products of sedimentation in tropical seas. Marble and quartzite occur in patchy, eroded outcrops throughout the Eagle Mountains near the southeastern corner of the park.

An even more common metamorphic rock in the park, possibly of equivalent age

Marble outcrops on the north flank of the Eagle Mountains reveal the original sedimentary layering of the Precambrian limestone from which it was metamorphosed.

to the marble and quartzite mentioned above, is a dark, banded rock called gneiss (pronounced "nice"). The bands in gneiss consist of dark minerals, such as hornblende and biotite, alternating with light-colored minerals such as quartz and plagioclase feldspar. Geologists still are not entirely sure how the banding develops, but they do know that gneiss forms only under conditions of substantially high pressure and temperature.

MOUNTAINS COME AND MOUNTAINS GO

In the metamorphic rocks of Joshua Tree, geologists believe that they are looking deep inside the remains of a long-eroded mountain range on an ancient supercontinental landmass which they call

Rodinia. Radiometric age dating shows that these rocks and the range they once formed existed nearly two billion years ago, long before any life crawled on the earth's land surface, and so long before the present that it is almost impossible to imagine. No one has yet named this former mountain range, although parts of it have been named in other regions.

Gneiss, one of the most common types of bedrock in Joshua Tree, exposed along the trail to the Lost Horse Mine. This is a cross-sectional "end view," revealing the multiple foliation planes.

It was certainly a remarkable group of mountains, stretching diagonally from what is now the Baltic region of northern Europe across North America from the eastern United States through southern California and into more distant western lands that have since been rifted from our continent by plate separation. This rifting

ORIGIN OF FOLIATION STRUCTURE IN GNEISS

SEDIMENTARY PARENT ROCK

METAMORPHIC MINERALS FORM

INTENSIVE FOLDING, SHEARING, RECRYSTALLIZATION AND PARTIAL MELTING FORM GNEISS

GNEISS STRUCTURE LINEATION IN FOLIATION PLANE

EXPOSED FOLIATION PLANE

SIDE OF ROCK SAMPLE REVEALS MULIPLE FOLIATION PLANES

event created the ancestral Pacific Ocean. Some geologists relate ancient gneisses in Australia to those found today in areas such as Joshua Tree, indicating that eastern Australia was at one time connected to California. Others have linked the gneiss to rocks found in the Trans–Antarctic Mountains, near the South Pole. Australia and Antarctica apparently were linked to western North America at one time. So it might be appropriate for our discussion to call the ancient metamorphosed mountains of Joshua Tree the Trans–Rodinian Mountains. The breakup of Rodinia and birth of the Pacific Ocean occurred about 800 million years ago, by which time the Trans–Rodinian range had probably already eroded into low, stony hills and wide, empty valleys. This landscape must have looked quite bleak indeed, for life, either in the form of plants or animals, had not yet colonized the earth's dry lands.

Following the rifting of Rodinia, the Joshua Tree region probably became a marine continental shelf with sediment settling atop the shallowly submerged bedrock and remained so for the next 550 million years.

WHEN THE WEST COAST WAS THE NORTH COAST

Geologists call the period of time between 545 million and 251 million years ago the Paleozoic Era (era of early life), because it was then that life began to thrive on both the land and in the seas. Furthermore, owing to plate motions, the western coast of today was the northern coast of North America. It lay near the equator in warm waters that promoted growth and development of vast reefs and limestone deposits. No equivalent-aged limestone beds have been found in Joshua Tree, but perhaps they did exist in the park region at one time and have been eroded away. The geographic position of the park suggests that it was underwater throughout much of Paleozoic time.

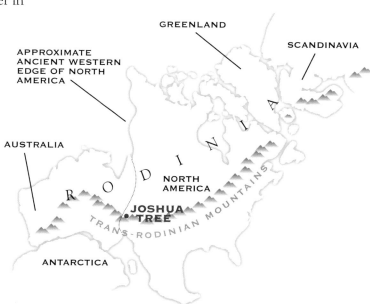

Reconstruction of the Rodinian landmass. This amalgamation of continents existed 1.7 billion to 800 million years ago, during which time the Joshua Tree gneisses were formed.
(After Brookfield, 1993; Karlstrom and others, 1999.)

SPOTTED GNEISS

"ORDINARY"
INJECTION GNEISS

MYLONITIC
TONALITE GNEISS

"FAULT GNEISS"
(MYLONITE)

GNEISSES SHOW A WIDE RANGE IN APPEARANCE, REFLECTING VARIATIONS IN THE SOURCE ROCKS FROM WHICH THEY FORM. THE GNEISS IN BLACK ROCK WASH AT THE WESTERN END OF THE PARK, FOR EXAMPLE, CONTAINS WELL-DEFINED BANDS OF LIGHT AND DARK MINERALS. IN CONTRAST, THE GNEISS NEAR THE OLD MINE TANK IN PLEASANT VALLEY ALONGSIDE GEOLOGY TOUR ROAD SHOWS WEAK OR PATCHY BANDING AND IS LIGHTER COLORED.

IT IS CLEAR THAT BANDING IN SOME GNEISSES FORMED WHERE SMALL AMOUNTS OF MOLTEN ROCK, PRODUCING THE LIGHT-COLORED MINERALS, INJECTED DARKER METAMORPHIC ROCK. SOME OF THE PLANES OF BANDING (FOLIATION PLANES) MAY REVEAL LINEATIONS OF LIGHT-COLORED MINERALS THAT INDICATE THE DIRECTION THAT THE ROCK STRETCHED IN RESPONSE TO STRESS. IN OTHER AREAS, FAULT ACTION WITHOUT MELTING CREATES A SPECIAL KIND OF GNEISS TERMED MYLONITE.

MOUNTAIN BUILDING AND ROCK MELTING — ROUND TWO

By 280 million years ago, North America had become part of another supercontinent called Pangaea, with Joshua Tree lying on the northwestern coast.

Supercontinents do not last very long, geologically speaking, because they trap heat from the earth's deep interior. As the heat builds up, rifting at the surface becomes inevitable. Beginning about 210 million years ago, Pangaea began splitting north-to-south, practically down the middle, and the sea flooded in, forming the young Atlantic Ocean. North America — merely a sundered fragment of Pangaea — shifted westward, squeezing its heretofore relatively quiet Pacific continental shelf. At the same time, the lithosphere beneath the shelf not far to the west of Joshua Tree cracked under the heavy load of sediments, and the Pacific sea floor began thrusting and sinking beneath a rapidly folding and rising shelf edge. Joshua Tree's half-billion years of being low-lying and submerged ended. The Nevadan Mountains, the geologic ancestor of most present-day mountain ranges in California, began growing along the edge of the continent. The ancient Rodinian rocks, also caught up in this mountain building, underwent renewed crumpling and heating. Some of the bedrock experienced a second round of metamorphism. One reason that the

15

1. GNEISSES FORM, MOUNTAINS GROW 1.7 TO 1.8 BILLION YEARS AGO

CRUST

MANTLE

2. LIFTING AND EROSION OF DEEP CRUST 1.7 BILLION TO 250 MILLION YEARS AGO

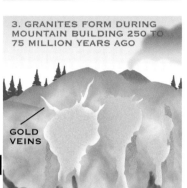

3. GRANITES FORM DURING MOUNTAIN BUILDING 250 TO 75 MILLION YEARS AGO

GOLD VEINS

4. RENEWED LIFTING AND EROSION OF DEEP CRUST 75 MILLION YEARS AGO TO PRESENT

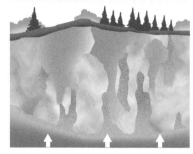

5. FAULTING AND BASALTIC INTRUSION OF CRUST, 25 MILLION YEARS AGO TO PRESENT

6. DRYING OUT OF CLIMATE TO DESERT CONDITIONS, TEN MILLION YEARS AGO TO PRESENT

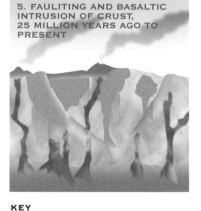

KEY

GNEISS | MOLTEN GRANITE | HARDENED GRANITE | MOLTEN BASALTIC INTRUSION | HARDENED BASALTIC INTRUSION | ACTIVE VOLCANO

Major mountain-building events in the Joshua Tree region.

gneisses in Joshua Tree reveal complexities, even to well-seasoned geologists, is that they record the imprints of not one, but two major mountain-building events.

OCEAN FLOOR TAKES A DIVE

The oceanic plate to the west was composed of basalt, a very dense rock that is typical of the ocean floor. Basalt, rich in iron and magnesium that help make it dark and heavy, is a product of partial melting in the earth's mantle, the very thick planetary layer lying between the earth's crust and its core. Basalt is more heavy and dense than both granite and gneiss, so the oceanic plate sank beneath North America as compression from Pangaea's breakup continued. The plate eventually slid eastward as far as Colorado and western Texas. In terms of depth, it probably sank intact as much as 400 miles (650 km) into the mantle. There, the foundering plate may have broken up, with pieces sinking some 1,900 miles (about 3,000 km) to the core–mantle boundary. Some geologists think that a 12,000-mile- (19,600 km) wide slab of ocean floor eventually disappeared beneath the deep marine trench marking the edge of the sinking plate along the California coast. Such a length of crust is equivalent to half the earth's circumference. Surely, the engulfment of this plate, with the consequent growth of the Nevadan Mountains, and, farther inland, the Rocky Mountains, was one of the great tectonic events in all of earth history. The outstanding record of this event in the Joshua Tree landscape is the granitic rocks that climbers and sightseers most enjoy.

MAKING GRANITE

Granite forms in stages beginning with a sinking oceanic plate, a process that geologists call subduction (under-moving). As the sea floor subducts beneath the edge of a continent, it carries along tremendous volumes of trapped seawater. The downgoing plate begins to heat up due to the immense frictional forces and because the mantle into which it sinks is already hot. Ultimately, the trapped seawater begins to boil out, percolating into the wedge of mantle that lies between the sinking plate and the overriding continent. Because moist rock melts more easily than dry rock, the infiltrating water causes some of the overlying mantle wedge to melt, forming basaltic and somewhat similar andesitic magma. (Magma, or

melt, is underground molten rock, essentially lava before it erupts). The molten basalt ascends into the metamorphosing chaos of gneiss and sedimentary layers above and thus introduces tremendous

THE ORIGIN OF BIG, PINK FELDSPAR CRYSTALS IN GRANITE

SOME JOSHUA TREE GRANITES CONTAIN HUGE CRYSTALS OF PINK ALKALI (POTASSIUM- AND SODIUM-RICH FELDSPAR), CALLED MEGACRYSTS, ENCLOSED BY COUNTLESS SMALLER MINERAL GRAINS. INDIVIDUAL MEGACRYSTS ARE UP TO SEVERAL INCHES IN LENGTH AND TYPICALLY HAVE NEARLY PERFECT RECTANGULAR SHAPES. SPECIAL CONDITIONS OF CHEMISTRY, PRESSURE, AND TEMPERATURE MUST EXIST TO PERMIT MEGACRYST GROWTH. FOR YEARS GEOLOGISTS HAVE PUZZLED OVER THESE UNUSUAL CRYSTALS. MANY GEOLOGISTS BELIEVE THAT MEGACRYSTS CRYSTALLIZE DIRECTLY FROM MAGMA. THE LARGE CRYSTAL SIZES COULD RESULT FROM SLOW COOLING OF THE MOLTEN ROCK DURING CRYSTALLIZATION. LOSS OF GAS OR THE ASCENT OF THE MAGMA TO A SHALLOWER LEVEL WHERE COOLING IS MORE RAPID WOULD CREATE THE FINER-GRAINED CRYSTALS SURROUNDING THE MEGACRYSTS. ALKALI FELDSPARS ARE ORDINARILY AMONG THE LAST MINERALS TO FORM IN A MAGMA. HOWEVER, THE NEARLY PERFECT SHAPES OF MOST MEGACRYSTS IMPLY THAT THEY DEVELOP EARLIER THAN THE OTHER CRYSTALS WITH WHICH THEY ARE FOUND. AN EXCELLENT PLACE TO VIEW MEGACRYSTIC ROCKS IS AT RATTLESNAKE CANYON JUST EAST OF INDIAN COVE CAMPGROUND.

amounts of fresh heat into an already warm crust.

Some of the magma may rise all the way to the earth's surface and build basaltic and andesitic volcanoes. Elsewhere the magma heats up the surrounding sedimentary and metamorphic rocks so much that they melt in huge volumes. The melt separates and rises through numerous vein-like channelways to collect at shallower levels in the crust as batches of distinctive secondary or continental magma. It is such relatively shallow-formed secondary magmas, heated by hotter material rising from below, that cooled, hardened, and eventually took the form of Joshua Tree's famous granites.

STIRRED AS WELL AS SHAKEN

Even a short tour through the park will reveal more than one type of granite. Some rocks contain big blocky crystals of pink feldspar. Other granitic rocks are darker, finer grained, and consist of crystals of uniform size. Most of these differences result from the blending of varying amounts of primary mantle and secondary continental magmas during crystallization. Rocks resulting from the blending of different parent magmas are termed hybrids, and hybridization refers to the magma-mixing process.

Many igneous rocks show a range of intermediate compositions between pure granite and basalt. While not all such compositions need form by hybridization,

there is increasing evidence that many do. At Joshua Tree, geologists identify such granitic rocks as syenogranites, monzo-granites, granodiorites, tonalites, and monzonites. The list is daunting, and the distinctions are often difficult to make. For simplicity's sake, we refer to all of them here simply as granite.

In some cases, magmas are so distinctly different that they won't blend when they come into contact with one another, but just mingle together. Typically, basaltic magma is hotter and more fluid than granitic magma and can form blobby masses as it invades molten granite. In places, isolated blobs of basaltic material, perhaps slightly hybridized, may circulate high up into the granitic melt, later to crystallize in place, forming rounded dark inclusions, called enclaves, within the granite. Such enclaves are common in some Joshua Tree granites. Elsewhere, highly angular inclusions of gneiss or other rocks included in

Enclaves in granite showing various stages in hybridization between basalt inclusions and the granitic host rock. Camera lens cap for scale.

granites must have originated by collapse of the walls or ceiling of a molten granite body. Geologists refer to this class of inclusions as xenoliths, or foreign rocks. These, too, are common in some Joshua Tree granites.

Granite magmas can form as deeply as 15 miles (25 km), then rise all the way to the surface where they may erupt in extremely powerful volcanic explosions, such as occurred in Yellowstone National Park 600,000 years ago. Most of the granite we see at Joshua Tree cooled and solidified some five to ten miles (8 to15 km) underground. We do not know if any of the Joshua Tree granitic magma formed shallower fingers that triggered Yellowstone-like eruptions, because all traces of such related volcanic vents, if they ever existed, have long since eroded away. Nevertheless, indirect evidence from elsewhere in the Mojave Desert suggests that Joshua Tree granite almost certainly did feed volcanoes.

THE PLUTON — NAMESAKE OF A GOD

The Joshua Tree granites did not form all at once, but incrementally over millions of years they ascended, cooled, and crystallized in separate masses, called plutons, after Pluto, the Roman god of the under world. A typical pluton is at least a few miles across. Some are zoned, with one kind of granite on the outside and another at the center. The zoning arises from vari-

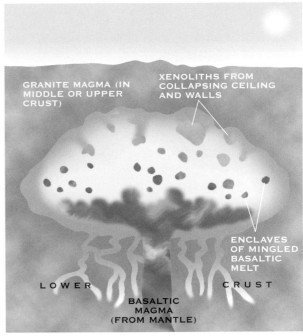

Two origins for inclusions in granite.

ous factors, perhaps indicating varying degrees of assimilation of the surrounding crust by the hot magma, changing amounts of partial melting in the magma source area, hybridization, piecemeal crystallization, or perhaps all of these processes acting together. Geologists have named some of the granite bodies after local landmarks, examples being the White Tank monzogranite at Jumbo Rocks, the Twentynine Palms quartz monzonite and the Oasis monzogranite at Fortynine Palms Oasis.

The Oasis monzogranite is the core of a much larger pluton. It includes beautiful silvery muscovite and numerous tiny dots of red garnet, a rare mineral in granitic rocks. The trail from the parking area at the end of Canyon Road to Fortynine

Palms Oasis crosses the northern edge of the pluton near the highest point on the trail. By careful observation, you may recognize that the pluton is zoned, with the granitic rock near its edge lacking garnet and muscovite but containing more abundant dark minerals, especially hornblende, than the monzogranite at trail's end.

SUBDUCTION — SLOWING DOWN FOR THE TIME BEING

Subduction of sea floor beneath southern California continued until about 25 million years ago. But granite magmas and associated building of the Nevadan Mountains ceased long before that. The angle of the subducting plate became much shallower about 75 million years ago, causing the long pause between the end of mountain building and plate collision. Such shallow subduction does not allow a wedge of mantle to be caught up in the melting process. Essentially, a shallow subducting plate can just scrape and bump against the underside of the continental lithosphere for hundreds of kilometers, like a whale edging against the bottom of a boat. Without mantle-derived magmas entering the crust, it is unlikely that granite magmas will form. The youngest granites emplaced in the Joshua Tree region are about 75 million years old. Furthermore, the compressive force from plate collision is spread over much broader regions than in the case of steep subduction. Instead of a rather narrow, high mountain range full

of intruding magmas and erupting volcanoes, shallow subduction creates very broad, blocky mountain systems with numerous faulted valleys and few active plutons. It was at this time, 75 million years ago, that the Nevadan Mountains stopped forming, and far inland, the Rocky Mountains began to grow — a direct consequence of the changing angle of the subducting plate.

Some 35 million years ago, the downgoing oceanic plate suddenly steepened again. The reason for the change is unknown, but it is likely due to the collision of India with Eurasia on the other side of the planet at about this time. This event may have radically rearranged the earth's internal currents. Whatever the reason, volcanic activity and related magma intrusions returned briefly to the western coast. Then, around 25 million years ago, rearrangement of plate boundaries began off the southern California coast, leading to the end of plate collision and the development of a side-sliding plate boundary across the region. The sliding boundary eventually became the San Andreas Fault.

A record of the brief flare-up of resurgent magma-related activity associated with the final stage of subduction is represented by lava flows along the northern and southern edges of the Pinto Basin, not far from the Old Dale and Black Eagle Mine roads, respectively. These lavas form mesas and bluffs. Some are similar in appearance to andesitic lavas that erupted

MAGMA, COOLING IN SHALLOW CRUST, MAY FORM CRACKS INTO WHICH MINERAL-RICH GROUND WATER MAY ENTER. EVENTUALLY, A VARIETY OF MINERALS CAN PRECIPITATE FROM THIS FLUID. WE SEE THE RESULT OF THIS DEEP-SEATED LAST GASP OF MAGMATIC ACTIVITY IN THE FORM OF NUMEROUS VEINS (REALLY JUST MINERAL-FILLED CRACKS) THAT CRISSCROSS THE GRANITE AND METAMORPHIC OUTCROPS OF THE JOSHUA TREE COUNTRYSIDE. GEOLOGISTS RECOGNIZE THREE BASIC VEIN TYPES: 1) PEGMATITES WITH LARGE CRYSTALS, SOMETIMES INCHES ACROSS; 2) APLITES WITH TINY CRYSTALS THAT TYPICALLY GIVE THE ROCK A SUGARY TEXTURE; AND 3) QUARTZ (OR QUARTZ-SULFIDE) VEINS, WHICH ARE MOSTLY MILKY WHITE, AND MAY CONTAIN GOLD OR SILVER AND SULFIDE MINERALS. IN THEIR SEARCH FOR GOLD, IT WAS THESE QUARTZ VEINS IN THE HIGHLANDS OF JOSHUA TREE THAT PROSPECTORS SOUGHT. MOST VEINS AT JOSHUA TREE STAND OUT PROMINENTLY AS NARROW WHITE BANDS AND STRIPES. MOST ARE MORE RESISTANT TO WEATHERING AND EROSION THAN THE SURROUNDING ROCKS, SO THEY ALSO FORM PROMINENT RIB LINES. THOSE INJECTED INTO GNEISS SHOW WILDLY MEANDERING SHAPES. THE ROCKY DESERT FLOOR BETWEEN STOP 6 ON THE GEOLOGY TOUR ROAD AND MALAPAI HILL IS AN EXCELLENT PLACE TO SEE APLITES AND PEGMATITES. PROMINENT APLITE VEINS CROP OUT ALONG THE ARCH ROCK GEOLOGY NATURE TRAIL AT WHITE TANK CAMPGROUND. APLITES AND PEGMATITES ALSO MAY BE SEEN IN BLACK ROCK WASH NEAR BLACK ROCK CAMPGROUND, AND IN PUSHAWALLA CANYON, WHICH IS REACHED BY FOLLOWING THE GEOLOGY TOUR ROAD INTO PLEASANT VALLEY.

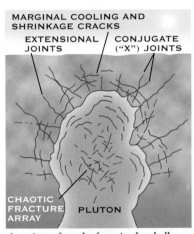

MARGINAL COOLING AND SHRINKAGE CRACKS
EXTENSIONAL JOINTS
CONJUGATE ("X") JOINTS
CHAOTIC FRACTURE ARRAY
PLUTON

A variety of cracks form in the shallow crust when magma intrudes. Fluids from the magma may fill the cracks to form pegmatites, aplites, and quartz veins. In many places, patterns are more complex than shown above.

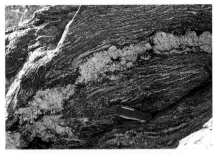

Pegmatite cutting across gneiss in Black Rock Wash.

This pegmatite vein contains gray quartz crystals (below coin), white feldspar crystals, and muscovite that looks like glittery reflections.

Aplite and pegmatite veins cut this weathered granite.

between 35 million and 15 million years ago and are found elsewhere in the Mojave. Geologists regard most andesite as evidence of subduction.

After the end of oceanic plate subduction, igneous activity in southern California waned. But minor injections of melt from the mantle continued to occur from time to time in the region because of crustal stretching and thinning along certain faults in southern California. This relieved pressure on the underlying rock material and triggered melting in the hot mantle below. The resulting igneous injections form the dark veins of basalt that cross the older granites and gneiss. In some locations, shallow masses of basaltic magma possibly were close enough to the surface to erupt. Malapai Hill, seen from the Geology Tour Road, could be an eruptive conduit. The top of the hill consists of basalt that contains fragments of peridotite, the rock type that makes up the earth's upper mantle. After rising into place, the cooling of the basalt created a set of regularly spaced fractures called columnar joints. The basalt forms a hill because it has not weathered as fast as the surrounding granite. Similar shallow basalt bodies exist near the Lost Horse Mine and Covington Flat.

Just how long ago Malapai Hill basalt intruded is unknown. Estimates vary from 100,000 to eight million years ago. Alteration of the volcanic rock by hot solutions makes it difficult to establish an age of formation. But almost certainly, injections of basalt magma have occurred much more recently in southern California. The youngest volcanoes close to Joshua Tree form a chain of small cinder cones that trend northeastward out of the Marine Corps Air Ground Combat Center at Twentynine Palms. The chain includes Dish Hill and Siberia Crater, small cinder

Malapai Hill, between Queen Valley (left) and Pleasant Valley (right), is a dark basaltic mass that intruded shallow granite crust.

cones along the National Trails Highway (the old Route 66). This volcanic chain was active about 2,000 years ago. Amboy Crater, about 30 miles (54 km) north of the park, is even younger, perhaps only a thousand years old.

To underscore the meaning of a long geologic record, imagine if the nearly two billion years of geologic change shown on the geologic column were represented by a line 300 feet (100 m) long. A segment far more narrow than the width of a hair

GEOLOGIC AGE			ROCK UNITS	GEOLOGIC EVENTS IN THE JOSHUA TREE REGION
CENOZOIC	QUATERNARY	HOLOCENE	dune sands, playa lake sediments, alluvial fans	10,000 years ago to the present: faulting, uplift and earthquakes; weathering, mass wasting and erosion add sediment to desert valleys and canyons as present arid climate established.
		0.01 Ma		
		PLEISTOCENE	playa lake sediments, alluvial fans.	Minor volcanism and major faulting in nearby areas of the Mojave Desert.
				Ice Age climate swings back and forth from glacial to warm interglacial extremes. Alluvium floods valleys and canyons during interglacials; alluvial fans form; pediments and inselbergs emerge as soil cover erodes.
		1.6 Ma		
	TERTIARY		alluvial fans being deposited	10 Ma to present: rise of coastal ranges and the Sierra Nevada creates rain shadow across Mojave region.
				10 – 25 Ma: warm, semiarid climate nurtures a savanna grassland in the Mojave region and promotes formation of thick soils on bedrock in the Joshua Tree region.
				25 – 30 Ma: Subduction ends as San Andreas fault begins to form.
				15 – 30 Ma: widespread volcanism throughout southern California, possibly including eruption of lava flows in Pinto and Hexie Mountains.
				50 Ma: Erosion begins widely exposing granite and gneiss. Plutonism ends.
	66 Ma			
MESOZOIC	CRETACEOUS		mafic and felsic dikes monzogranite of 49 Palms Oasis White Tank monzogranite Queen Mountain monzogranite	Continued subduction and plutonism along the entire western edge of the North American plate. (Cretaceous granites make up most of the cores of today's Sierra Nevada, San Bernardino and Little San Bernardino Mountains.)
(Age of Queen Mountain pluton uncertain; it may be Jurassic)
	144 Ma			
	JURASSIC		Gold Park diorite	Continued subduction and plutonism.
	200 Ma			
	TRIASSIC		Twentynine Palms megacrystic quartz monzonite	About 250 Ma: subduction of the oceanic plate beneath the North American plate initiates plutonism in western North America. Nevadan Mountains begin forming.
	251 Ma			
PALEOZOIC			(no record)	Probable marine sedimentation, but record removed by erosion.
	545 Ma			
PRECAMBRIAN	PROTEROZOIC		various gneisses, marble, quartzite	800 Ma: breakup of Rodinia. Joshua Tree region a young continental shelf probably receiving sediments derived from erosion of the Trans-Rodinian mountains.
1870 to 1650 Ma: Trans-Rodinian mountains form in the region accompanied by metamorphism and plutonism.

Geologic column of major geologic events and rock units in the Joshua Tree National Park region. Ma = one million years.

would represent the last two hundred years, the time of recorded human history in southern California.

BEDROCK BREAKUP

Geologists use the terms joints and faults to describe natural cracks in bedrock. Joints differ from faults, which are a class of especially huge cracks, because little slippage of rock occurs along joints when they form, whereas along faults, blocks of crust may slide for miles past one another. Normally, joints and faults have surfaces underground that form planes that, in detail, may be smooth to rough, and locally may curve or bend sharply. Of course, we are unable to see these deeply buried surfaces because they are sealed tightly in bedrock. But, with the passage of time, erosion and weathering partially expose them and eventually create open fractures. Many climbing routes in the park have been designed deliberately by rock climbers to take advantage of these geologic features.

Fractured bedrock in Pushawalla Wash. Tensional stress caused by erosion of the adjacent wash together with outward wedging of the slope by plant roots (note the tree on the left) probably caused the vertical fractures. Horizontal cracks originated as lift joints.

JOINTS — RESULTS OF PUSH AND PULL

Joints commonly display systematic orientations. We can reasonably assume that all joints that show the same general pattern in their orientations have formed from the same general process. Stretching or squeezing of the earth's crust probably cause most joints.

CONJUGATE JOINTS

During plate collision, squeezing of the crust will cause it to break into sets of cracks that crisscross one another, intersecting at angles of 60 and 120 degrees. Such an intersecting pattern of joints in rock outcroppings resembles giant Xs. The bisectors of the 60-degree angles in each X indicate the directions from which compressive stresses (squeezing forces) operated to produce the joints. Because both of the joints crossing in an X-pattern form simultaneously due to crustal compression, geologists call them conjugate (together-forming) joints.

When hiking along the Hidden Valley Nature Trail, you'll see many conjugate joints exposed in the granite cliff faces and along the trail. The X patterns indicate that most, if not all, must have formed from compressive stresses acting at a high angle to the present surface of the earth, in other words, closer to vertical than horizontal. A logical deduction from this observation is that these joints formed during a period of uplift that has brought the granite upward many miles from its point of origin to its present position where erosion has exposed it. The granite was being squeezed from two directions as the joints formed: from below by the forces of uplift, and from above simply by the weight of the many miles of original overlying rock.

It is uncertain when these joints formed, but obviously they postdate the cooling of the granite that they slice across. Consequently, we can constrain the possible age of the joints by acknowledging several known facts and making a few reasonable assumptions. Geologists believe that conjugate joints can form no deeper than about eight to ten miles (13 to 16 km) beneath the surface because below this depth, the earth is too warm for cracking to take place. It also happens that this is a reasonable estimate for the original depth of the magma that cooled to form much of the granite in Joshua Tree country, based upon specialized study of certain constituent mineral compositions.

Let us consider that we have determined by radiometric dating that a particular Joshua Tree granite is 100 million years old. We can be reasonably sure from what we've learned about how mountains grow that the uplifting forces were already active as our granite cooled and hardened. Thus, the conjugate joints that we see in the granite could be virtually as old as the rock itself. On the other hand, some, if not all, could have formed much later, up until

erosion had removed so much of the overlying rock that the granite was buried only a few hundred feet (100 to 200 m), a depth at which another class of joints (those that are more flat-lying) began forming.

How long does it take nature to erode away a few hundred feet of rock? The rates vary greatly according to slope, climate, and rock type. In the Joshua Tree region, we know that rocks formed about ten miles (16km) down are now at the surface. If our 100-million-year-old granite also originated at a depth of ten miles (16 km), there would be a mean erosion rate of one mile (1.6 km) every ten million years or a half foot (15 cm) every thousand years. From other geologic evidence visible in the Joshua Tree region, such an erosion rate seems reasonable, although in the present arid climate it would almost certainly be too high. This suggests that granite we now see on the surface, such as in Hidden Valley, was deep enough to form conjugate joints as recently as 500,000 to a million years ago, the time it would take to erode off a few hundred feet (100 to 200 m) of overburden using our estimate. Obviously, 500,000 to 100 million years is a wide time range in which the conjugate Xs that crisscross the granite could form. However, this scenario illustrates the sort of reasoning geologists must use and the uncertainties they often face in answering questions about the development of natural landscapes.

Lift Joints

That the conjugate joints at Joshua Tree must have formed over a broad span of time seems likely, given the fact that a variety of different stress points can be discerned from looking at them. Most inferred directions of compression are oriented quite steeply; but even on a small scale, such as in Hidden Valley, one can see that they do not all show the same exact orientation. Some joint sets seem to be superposed on older ones with slightly different orientations. The detailed history of how the earth has lifted up Joshua Tree's granites is indeed complex and probably may never be fully understood.

When uplift and erosion bring buried bedrock to within a few hundred feet of the surface, another type of joint begins forming. These joints develop under vertical tension. They consist of a series of nearly horizontal cracks that are roughly parallel to both one another and to the overlying surface of the earth, and are called lift or relaxation joints.

Imagine yourself sitting on a soft sofa. Your body weight presses down the underlying cushion in much the same way that rock is squeezed deep inside the earth. As you stand up, the cushion expands,

ORIGIN OF JOINTS (FRACTURES) IN ROCK

Stretching of a rectangular block of rock causes it to break at a right angle to the direction of the stretching.

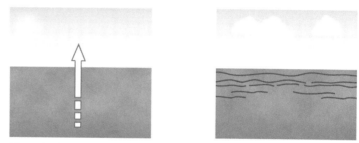

Upward relaxation of the crust in response to erosion of overlying rocks causes it to break into lift joints that parallel the earth's surface.

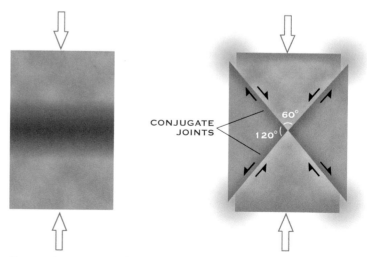

CONJUGATE JOINTS

60°
120°

Compression causes it to break into a set of cross-cutting fractures called conjugate joints.

relaxing upward thanks to the removal of your weight. Likewise, when erosion removes the rock overlying a given mass of crust, the crust begins to expand and relax. But it is brittle rock, not a soft cushion, and as it expands it breaks into lift joints. The joints form perpendicular to the direction of tensional stress responsible for their formation. (Note the contrast between lift joints and conjugate shears in terms of what they relate about original stress directions.)

Consider the variation in stress directions over time when you see lift joints superimposed over an older conjugate set. Add to that the irregularities of the intersecting surface topography that occur throughout the park, and you can readily appreciate why the joint patterns you see in the bedrock are so bafflingly complex. Nevertheless, some sense may be made out of trying to understand them.

The system of joints in the bedrock of Joshua Tree breaks it into blocks, cubes, and other less regular shapes. The active agents of weathering and erosion exploit this network of joints to round out the individual blocks of crust and eventually isolate them as large surface boulders. This explains the origin of the spectacular rock-scrambling terrain found at the Wonderland of Rocks, Jumbo Rocks, and the area around Mastodon Peak near Cottonwood Spring.

FLOATING MOUNTAINS

What caused bedrock to rise five to ten miles (8 to 16 km) in the Joshua Tree area? And what happened to the shallower rock that overlaid it?

Answering these questions requires returning to the theory of plate tectonics. As plates collide, the colliding edge of a continental plate will thicken due to folding and faulting of the lithosphere. At the surface, huge mountains will grow; but unseen below is an even greater mass of continental lithosphere extending downward into the hot, soft, plastic mantle. In other words, mountains grow downward into the warm, squishy, puttylike deep earth as well as upward into the sky. In fact, there is much more downward growth than upward! Geologists refer to the

COMPLEX JOINT PATTERNS FORMED BY VARIOUS COMBINATIONS OF JOINT SETS, ASSUMING A UNIFORM STRESS FIELD EXISTED AS EACH JOINT SET FORMED

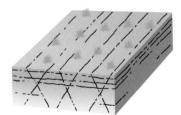

Conjugate joints formed by vertically directed compression combined with lift joints.

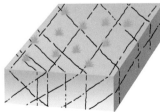

Conjugate joints formed by horizontally directed compression combined with a set of vertical tension joints.

Here there are three different joint sets. Both the strength and stress orientations present in the crust tend to vary widely, even over short distances, resulting in yet more complexity than illustrated.

pendulant, lithospheric bottom of a mountain belt as a mountain root.

Similar to icebergs floating at sea, a mountain belt floats on the mantle. And just as an iceberg mass maintains itself above sea level, due to the difference in the densities of ice and water, so too does a certain mass of continental material maintain itself above the level of the surrounding crust in the form of high mountains, owing to the difference in densities between lithosphere and mantle. Imagine what would happen if you could shave off the top of an iceberg with a giant cutting tool; the root of the berg, extending into the ocean below, would buoy up to compensate for the sudden reduction in ice above; i.e., as ice melts it continues to maintain the same ratio of mass above the waterline to the mass below. In fact, you could continue shaving ice off the top until practically none remained at all, above or below the waterline.

Nature provides a great shaving tool to cut down mountains and to force their roots to float upward: erosion. Once plate collision slows or stops, downcutting streams, landsliding, and other forms of erosion begin to reduce the height of the mountains. Ultimately, the sediment is swept out to sea or, if the climate is too arid for streams to travel that far, the sediment is carried at least as far as nearby valleys and basins.

It is important to appreciate that even though the bedrock of Joshua Tree has risen as much as 15 miles (25 km) since its time of origin, there are reasons that there never were mountains 15 miles high in this region: (1) it takes only a little erosion to cause a lot of uplift of an underlying mountain root; and, (2) erosion was occurring throughout and continuously after the period of plate collision. Thus, the deep bedrock of Joshua Tree has floated and shifted upward into an erosive shaving tool, which is still active at the surface although somewhat slowed under today's arid conditions.

Buoyancy of ancient mountain roots, both Trans–Rodinian and Nevadan, together with the more recent

Weathering of bedrock into soil (brown) occurs preferentially along joints. Subsequent erosion removes the loose soil, creating a landscape of rounded boulders, a rock scrambler's delight.

This boulder west of Stop 7 on the Geology Tour Road, is a remnant core-stone. We know, from the quartz vein outcropping in the bedrock "floor" that aligns upward with a remnant of the same vein in the boulder, that this boulder retains its original geometric relationship to the underlying bedrock.

Transverse Range uplift explains why such deep crustal rocks appear at the surface in Joshua Tree. What are the relative contributing effects of each of these agencies? Because some of the gneisses have undergone at least two episodes of mountain building, erosion, and root uplift, we should expect them to represent the deepest crustal rocks exposed in the park. The gneiss in the Hexie Mountains, for example, formed 15 miles (25 km) down. Because the later granites which intrude this gneiss formed at a depth of about ten miles (16 km), this indicates that five miles (8 km) of uplift occurred between the late Precambrian and Mesozoic mountain-building events. Fault motion, as well as simple root bouyancy, accounts for this uplift. Moving to more recent times, fault-related uplift of the Transverse Ranges probably accounts for somewhat less than half the ten miles of bedrock uplift inferred for the granites. The rest of this uplift is due primarily to adjustment of the ancient Nevadan mountain root. These rough estimates help put some dimensions on the statement that a visit to Joshua Tree National Park is a journey deep into Earth's crust.

FAULTS

The San Andreas Fault stretches 700 miles (1,100 km) from the Gulf of California to Cape Mendocino north of San Francisco. It marks the boundary between the North American Plate to the east, and the Pacific Plate on the west, and includes most of coastal central and southern California. At present, the plates are trying to ease past one another along this great tear at a rate of one-fourth to almost two inches (50 to 480 mm) per year. The San Andreas is a dynamic system that has not always followed its present course. The San Andreas fault zone began forming off the southern California coast 25 to 30 million years ago, and has since migrated inland, jumping from position to position every few million years, activating the traces of older faults or creating new ones while so doing. Ever-bigger pieces of the North American Plate have been bitten off and added to the Pacific Plate in the process. Most former traces of the San Andreas Fault boundary lie to the west of its present location. Both the San Gabriel Fault near Los Angeles, and the San Gregorio–Hosgri Fault farther north, once served as the plate boundary. Both faults, too, are now nearly dead, abandoned as all the action has shifted inland. Within Joshua Tree, the Dillon Fault may mark an earlier position of the plate boundary. Geologists are uncertain if the Dillon Fault, like the San Gregorio– Hosgri and San Gabriel Faults, is now past its prime, although most geologists do not consider it a major seismic risk.

WATCH OUT FOR THE ASPERITIES

Wherever the San Andreas Fault maintains a straight northwest-southeast course through California, the plates slide past one another without undergoing huge amounts of compression or tension along their edges. Big earthquakes certainly do occur from time to time, but this is due to the nature of the fault plane, which extends some nine miles (15 km) into the crust and is not a perfectly smooth surface. Instead, the fault plane is rather "sticky," roughened by irregular rock edges, called asperities, against which the sliding plates become locked until enough pressure has been built to overcome resistance. When that happens, the crust gives way in a big, energy-releasing earthquake. During the magnitude-8.25 Fort Tejon

OUT TO SEA

CALIFORNIA

SAN ANDREAS FAULT

SAN FRANCISCO

RINCONADA-RELIZIAN FAULT

SAN GREGORIO-HOSGRI FAULT

THE "BIG BEND" EAST-WEST STRETCH OF THE SAN ANDREAS FAULT

JOSHUA TREE NAT. PARK

SANTA BARBARA

LOS ANGELES

SAN GABRIEL FAULT

SAN DIEGO

EASTERN BEND

TO THE GULF OF CALIFORNIA

DILLON FAULT

Trace of the San Andreas Fault and related fault strands through California. Arrows indicate relative motions of the North American and Pacific Plates along the San Andreas Bend, causing uplift of the Transverse Ranges.

Looking from Keys View across the Coachella Valley toward Mt. San Jacinto. The linear hills extending from left to right across the center of the photograph mark the trace of the San Andreas Fault.

earthquake in 1857, for example, coastal California slid nearly 30 feet (10 m) past the interior of the state in a matter of three terrifying minutes. The ground rupture extended about 250 miles (400 km) along the fault, although it did not reach as far south as Joshua Tree. Fortunately, few Californians lived outside of the San Francisco area at the time (Los Angeles had only about 10,000 residents), so there were few fatalities.

PLATES OF EQUAL WEIGHT

The San Andreas is not straight along its entire length. In southern California it changes course at the Big Bend and trends nearly east-west. Along this stretch of the fault, the two plates are squeezed together in a collision as well as sliding past one another. Because both plates consist of continental rock, one cannot subduct into the mantle beneath the other. Instead, both plates have broken into deep basins and mountain blocks as they attempt to negotiate the bend in the plate boundary, giving southern California its uniquely rugged topography. Many of the basins have been filled with enormous thicknesses of sediment eroded from adjoining highlands.

ALONG THE EDGE

Along the plate boundary, the plate edges have crumpled into the Transverse Ranges, of which several distinct segments are in the park. Valleys lying between these small mountain branches are of two types, those that have been shaped by erosion (Queen Valley in the central part of the park), and those that are formed by down dropping along faults (Pleasant Valley, between the Hexie and Little San Bernardino Mountains).

The elevations of the mountains in the

Transverse Ranges roughly correspond to the amount of compressive strain built up along the crosscutting San Andreas Fault. West of the Big Bend, the mountains are of only moderate height (3,000 to 8,000 feet; 915 to 2,400 m) but summits to the east attain their maximum elevation in the range (to 11,700 feet; 3,567 m). Passing farther to the east into the Joshua Tree region, elevations drop again, however, due to a gentle southward curve in the San

Andreas between Palm Springs and Indio, plus the presence of many smaller faults that more widely disperse the stresses leading to mountain building.

Unlike the earlier Rodinian and Nevadan mountain building events, uplift of the Transverse Ranges has neither formed a deep lithospheric root, as far as we can determine, nor accompanied significant metamorphism or igneous activity, because subduction is not involved. The mountains of Joshua Tree owe their existence to a geometrically imperfect and unstable plate boundary.

The San Andreas Fault passes within a few miles of the southwestern edge of the park. Its general position may be seen from Keys View on a clear day as a straight alignment of low hills cutting across the floor of Coachella Valley. Both the valley and the Santa Rosa–San Jacinto Mountains that form the horizon beyond are examples of the unique and dramatic topography imposed in the adjacent Pacific Plate by the San Andreas Bend.

ONE BIG FAULT LEADING TO OTHERS

In addition to the San Andreas, Joshua Tree National Park is surrounded by other active or recently active faults, and most of these are related in some way to the San Andreas fault system, past or present.

The most recent large earthquake along the San Andreas in the Joshua Tree region took place around A.D. 1680. Offset

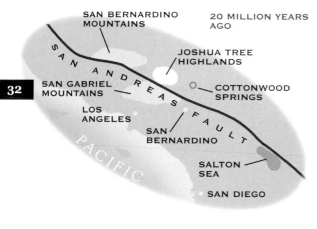

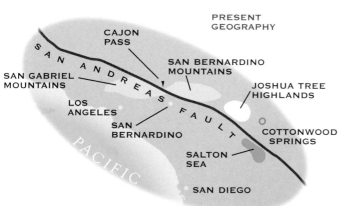

Speculative reconstruction of the Transverse Ranges to their positions about 20 million years ago.

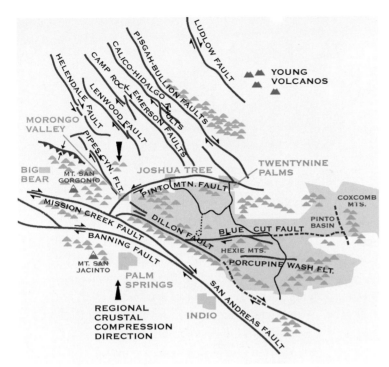

Major faults in the Joshua Tree region. The pattern of faulting makes sense to geologists who consider it in terms of compression (squeezing) from north to south. The faults near Morongo Valley, in particular, resemble a giant conjugate system. Both the Banning and Mission Creek Faults are strands of the San Andreas. They merge into the main fault just west of Indio.

strata along the fault that can be age dated indicate that such big quakes occur on an average of about once every 220 years. By that measure, then, Joshua Tree may be about due to be rocked again by major plate motion. In fact, recent magnitude-7 earthquakes in 1992 and 1999 along faults north of the park must reflect the buildup of strain along the nearby plate boundary. The San Andreas Fault does not slip with the regularity of a ticking clock, so the above statistic is somewhat misleading. Nonetheless, future earthquakes will certainly happen.

In all, the crust has shifted about a hundred miles (160 km) along this stretch of the San Andreas Fault. Were that net fault slippage to be undone, it would move much of Joshua Tree National Park back to just north of the San Gabriel Mountains, and much closer to Los Angeles.

FAULTS IN MOTION

To describe the displacement observed along a fault, geologists compare how the crust on one side of it has moved relative to the crust on the other side. Faults can be divided into three broad categories based upon their manner of slipping. (See illustrations on following pages.) Those that involve merely horizontal slippage are termed lateral-slip faults, of which there are two types: left lateral and right lateral.

Faults that involve only vertical motion are called dip-slip faults, of which there are two types: normal and reverse. Normal faults result from horizontally directed stretching in the crust, whereas reverse faults result from horizontally directed compression.

Many faults are a combination of basic motions, and consequently exhibit so-called oblique slip. In the Joshua Tree landscape, each of these types of faults may be found, but the largest, most recently active faults are of lateral-slip character.

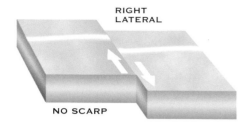

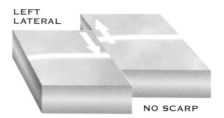

FINDING FAULTS

The Dillon and Blue Cut Faults slice southeast and east-west respectively across the southern portion of the park. These are the longest faults within the park boundaries, and they appear to be the most active.

The Dillon Fault is a right-lateral-slip fault, like the neighboring San Andreas. In fact, the Dillon Fault may be regarded as part of the San Andreas fault zone that branches off slightly into the Little San Bernardino Mountains. The left-lateral-slip Blue Cut Fault, in turn, branches off the Dillon Fault. It passes just south of Keys View, through Pleasant Valley and into Pinto Basin. The fault is named for a low pass at the southwest end of Pleasant Valley, easily seen from the Geology Tour Road, in which an extensive area of light-bluish-gray granitic rock is exposed.

Matching similar rocks exposed on opposite sides of the Blue Cut Fault reveals that as much as four miles (6 km) of left-lateral slip took place along the fault between Jurassic and Quaternary time. A branch of the Blue Cut forms the steplike fault scarps at the foot of the Hexie Mountains along the southwest edge of the Pinto Basin. Offsets of a late Pleistocene alluvial fan reveal that several rupture events occurred on the Blue Cut between 50,000 and 8,000 years ago. There is no indication of fault activity on the Blue Cut Fault during the past 8,000 years.

The Pinto Mountain Fault, trending nearly east-west along the north boundary of the park, is one of the most prominent faults other than the San Andreas itself. The fault is followed closely by the Twentynine Palms Highway (State Highway 62) between Twentynine Palms

DIP-SLIP FAULTS

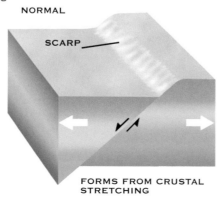

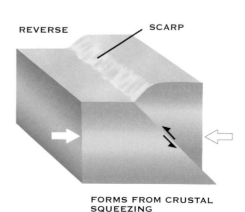

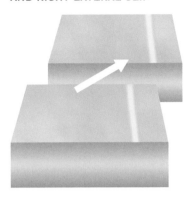

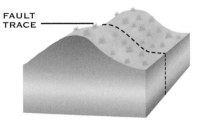

FAULT
TRACE

BEFORE SLIP

SCARP

AFTER SLIP

and Morongo Valley. In Morongo Valley and Yucca Valley, probable offset left-stepping stream channels mark the fault, but alluvial fill buries much of the evidence of the fault between Yucca Valley and Copper Mountain. A line of vegetation just west of Copper Mountain marks the position of the fault. Copper Mountain itself owes its existence to fault-related up-arching. Also, a one-mile-long (1.6 km) escarpment has been formed by the fault along the south side of Copper Mountain. In Twentynine Palms, a line of vegetation about 1.5 miles (2.4 km) long and a fault scarp about a half-mile (few hundred meters) long and up to ten feet (3 m) high marks the position of the fault at the Oasis of Mara, immediately west of the park service's

Oasis Visitor Center. This ledge may only be a couple of thousand years old, the product of a massive earthquake centered right at the site of Twentynine Palms.

The Red Cloud thrust is one of the oldest, most significant, but least discernable faults in the park. A thrust fault is merely a reverse fault whose surface dips very gently (less than 15 degrees) underground. Because of the low angle, surface traces of thrust faults tend to be highly irregular as

35

The only evidence of an inactive fault may be a straight contact between different rock types.

Many streams channels follow easily eroded fault lines.

Steplike fault scarps cutting the base of the Hexie Mountains mark two branches of the Blue Cut Fault. Viewed from Park Road near the Cholla Cactus Garden.

they cut across rugged country such as that at Joshua Tree. Although the fault is obscure, its juxtaposition to two large crustal masses of highly different rocks betrays its presence. One mass, the metamorphic Joshua Tree terrane and associated intrusive igneous rocks, dominates the underlying crust whereas the deeper-forming gneiss of the San Gabriel terrane dominates the overthrusted crust.

Erosion has exposed the lower Joshua Tree terrane in most of the park, although remnants of the San Gabriel terrane, bounded by the Red Cloud thrust and other faults exist in the Hexie, Cottonwood, and Eagle Mountains.

The age of the Red Cloud thrust is uncertain but the

The 1992 Landers earthquake (magnitude 7.5) created this 6.5-foot (2 m) vertical scarp due to a 14-foot (4.3 m) right lateral offset of a ridge.

extreme compression required to form thrust faults indicates that it must have formed during one of the major mountain-building episodes. Because Mesozoic plutons cut the thrust just east of Jumbo Rocks, it is clear that the fault can be no younger than Mesozoic, perhaps forming during the early phase of Nevadan mountain building.

Movement along larger faults rarely takes place along razor-sharp breaks in the rock. Instead, slices of rock caught between two oppositely moving masses of crust are crushed into a gray, powdery mass called gouge. Gouge is easily removed by stream erosion. Hence, many streams follow faults, cutting deep canyons that commonly are remarkably straight relative to other canyons in a region. A band of gouge from only a few inches to many yards wide may be the only indication that a fault crosses the area. The Fault Trail near Black Rock Campground follows a particularly spectacular example of fault-zone gouge.

SPRINGS AND OASES

Many of the major and minor fault zones serve to localize springs. Movement along faults creates impervious zones of pulverized rock fragments that form subsurface barriers, underground dams blocking groundwater flow and causing it to rise along a fault's upslope side. The Oasis of Mara at Twentynine Palms, Fortynine Palms Oasis, and the palm oasis at

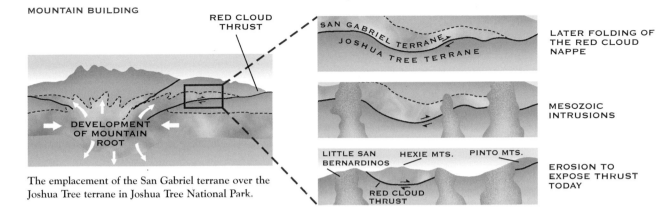

LATER FOLDING OF
THE RED CLOUD
NAPPE

MESOZOIC
INTRUSIONS

EROSION TO
EXPOSE THRUST
TODAY

RED CLOUD
THRUST

The emplacement of the San Gabriel terrane over the
Joshua Tree terrane in Joshua Tree National Park.

Cottonwood Springs, for example, are localized by fault-zone fissures along which ground water may reach the surface.

Determining how long springs have been active is fraught with difficulties, but we do know that some are of great age. Active springs may create deposits of tufa, porous, unlayered calcium carbonate formed by evaporation of water. Tufa mounds mark the sites of inactive springs. Some insight into the antiquity of springs comes from radiocarbon age determinations of tufa at nearly extinct Wood Spring near Cottonwood Oasis. Deposits here yield ages 21,000 to 14,000 years, suggesting that the spring was very active during the cooler and wetter climate of the last full-glacial maximum about 18,000 years ago.

Because life teems around springs the interplay of fault geology and biology is especially notable in Joshua Tree's desert landscape. The largest plants in the park, Washington (California) fan palms, are virtually all localized around fault-controlled springs, the seeds being transported from spring to spring in the digestive tracts of birds or coyotes or deliberately planted in earlier days by American Indians or immigrants. The natural colonization and migration of fan palms to new oases has continued into historical times.

THE OASIS OF MARA

PINTO MOUNTAIN FAULT SCARP AT THE
OASIS OF MARA IN TWENTYNINE PALMS.
THE PEOPLE ARE STANDING AT THE BASE
OF THE SCARP THAT FORMS THE STEP IN
THE LANDSCAPE. GROUND WATER
IMPOUNDED BY THE FAULT ACCOUNTS FOR
THE ALIGNMENT OF PALM TREES AND
OTHER VEGETATION. SUCH A FRESH SCARP
IS PROBABLY ONLY A FEW THOUSAND
YEARS OLD. THE HILL IN THE DISTANCE TO
THE RIGHT IS A PRESSURE RIDGE
SQUEEZED UP BY ACTION OF THE FAULT.

37

Sculpting the Desert Landscape

Perhaps the most impressive aspects of Joshua Tree National Park are the strange and picturesque shapes assumed by the bold granitic rock masses at Hidden Valley, Jumbo Rocks, Split Rock, and elsewhere. The sculpturing of these interesting rock masses is the result of the combined action of rock jointing and chemical and mechanical weathering. Rocks exposed at the earth's surface are not in their place of origin, and therefore are somewhat unstable in the surface environment. The gases in the atmosphere, changing temperatures, and rain and snow gradually attack and change rocks into something else. For example, rainwater, which is slightly acidic, will change the feldspar in granite to clays by a chemical process called hydrolysis.

Other minerals present in granite experience similar chemical changes, but at varying rates. In the case of the weathering of potassium feldspar, the clay mineral formed is kaolinite. It is soft and powdery compared to the original feldspar, and promotes disintegration of rock, especially along highly exposed edges and corners.

In contrast, milky quartz veins do not undergo hydrolysis. Hence, quartz veins, being chemically resistant, stand out boldly from the faces of granite.

Weathering occurs at the surface and underground, working along the rock joint planes as deep as a few tens of yards. The result is that blocks of buried, joint-bounded rock that were originally cubic in shape gradually become spherical as they weather into clay and grit, a process known as spheroidal weathering. The spheres are called core-stones. Examples of spheroidal weathering are common in many washes in Joshua Tree where erosion has cut deep into the ground.

Incipient spheroidal weathering exposed in a highway cut. Note the nearly right-angle intersections of the joints and the development of rounded core-stones.

Some rocks, like limestone and marble, may dissolve away completely as a result of chemical weathering. But others, like granite, only partially decompose, leaving

A young pinyon pine sinks its roots deep into a granite joint, wedging it open.

behind a loose residue of grus (coarse bits of granite that are gravel- to sand-sized fragments) and soil (powdered bits of granite and clay minerals that have formed by the hydrolysis of feldspar plus the addition of organic matter). Examples of grus formation are spectacular along the Panorama Loop Trail near Black Rock Wash. In addition to chemical weathering, plant roots (amazingly strong tissue!) wedge apart joints, and ice formed in joints during the winter months further disintegrates rock purely by brute force.

EXFOLIATION DOMES

Locally, granite bedrock may be less intensively jointed than in other places. Weathering cannot disintegrate such rock as rapidly as it does the surrounding, more broken crust. Consequently, the granite may develop extensive curved shells of rock along lift joints as erosion exposes it.

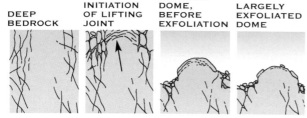

DEEP BEDROCK — INITIATION OF LIFTING JOINT — EXPOSED DOME, BEFORE EXFOLIATION — LARGELY EXFOLIATED DOME

Origin of granite exfoliation domes.

After exposure, further weathering, and erosion remove the outer casing of jointed rock, a process called exfoliation. The rounded mass of relatively unjointed granite remaining is called an exfoliation dome.

Yosemite National Park is famous for many towering exfoliation domes, including Basket Dome and Half Dome, the latter having been eroded in half by a past glaciation. Smaller, but still impressive domes also exist at Joshua Tree.

A dome at Barker Dam reservoir in the Wonderland of Rocks. The summit, which is part of its casing of exfoliating rock, is still intact.

SOIL—A VITAL PRODUCT OF WEATHERING

Soil, a loose mixture of mineral grains and organic material, if left undisturbed on the bedrock from which it is forming, will develop into layers, called soil horizons, that represent varying degrees and maturation of chemical weathering. The basal C horizon marks the transition between unweathered bedrock and the A and B horizons, mark a mature soil. The C horizon commonly consists of blocks of rock, some very large, immersed in their own weathering residues. The A and B horizons are of vital importance to plants, because it is from clays and decaying organic matter in these horizons that plants draw their nutrients. The decay of organic matter is promoted by microorganisms that play a critical role in the nutrient recycling process. Without continuous natural biological recycling of nutrients, the soil would become sterile and the plants would die.

While plant roots from the A and B horizons remove some nutrients, downward percolating ground water dissolves others. The dissolved nutrients do not travel far, however. Two processes force them to precipitate as new mineral grains within the B and C horizons. One process is evaporation, which we ordinarily think of as being confined to the surface but, in fact, can also take place at shallow depths. The other process is evapotranspiration, which is the loss of moisture to the atmosphere through plant tissues.

In arid climates, evaporation tends to play a greater role than biological activity in forcing mineral precipitation at the base of soils. This leads to marked differences between soil horizon compositions in arid versus humid climates. In temperate moist climates, the precipitated minerals are mostly dark iron oxides, but in arid regions the precipitate is primarily light-colored calcium carbonate (made up of the mineral calcite).

Thick accumulations of calcium carbonate in desert soils form caliche, a concrete-like, impermeable mass which may be several feet thick and thousands of years old. When exposed, caliche indicates erosion and near removal of no-longer stable soil cover.

NOTCHES

At Joshua Tree and other desert regions underlain by granitic bedrock, evidence of ancient soil horizons that existed some 10,000 to 20,000 years ago may be seen as linear dissolution marks and subsoil notches from which these soils, previously moist for long periods of time, have long since been eroded. The acids produced by living organisms or biological processes active in moist soils are especially corrosive to granite. There is an enormous contrast between subsoil (moist) and subaerial (dry) weathering rates of granitic rocks.

Undercutting of vertical rock faces, common on the shady sides of granitic rock outcroppings, may also be attributed to the action of subsoil moisture trapped at the base of the vertical face. Such undercutting probably accounts for many of the steep faces, as the processes of

SOIL LAYERING ASSOCIATED WITH WARM, HIGH-RAINFALL CLIMATES

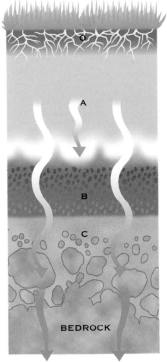

O HORIZON — Decaying vegetation, roots, microbial activity.

A HORIZON — "Zone of leaching." Downward percolating water removes many elements from clay minerals, making them available for plant roots to absorb. Elements, such as calcium, sodium, magnesium, potassium, iron, aluminum and silicon dioxide, also flush to deeper levels in the soil.

B HORIZON — "Zone of accumulation." Iron and aluminum oxides form here, in part supplied by leaching from above. Clays accumulate, other elements percolate through.

C HORIZON — The bedrock weathering zone. Elements flushed from above, plus some released during the weathering process, pass along joints and fractures in the bedrock to eventually reach the water table, making "hard water."

41

SOIL LAYERING ASSOCIATED WITH DRY, HOT CLIMATES

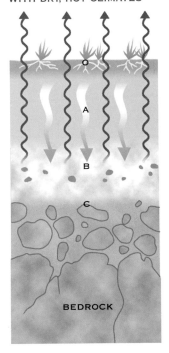

O HORIZON — Plant decay and microbial activity far less than in warm, humid climates.

A HORIZON — Leaching is less intensive in this layer than in warm humid climates. Extensive flushing of calcium to underlying B-horizon.

B HORIZON — Zone of accumlation of calcium, which combines with carbon dioxide, much of it stored in soil pores, to form an impermeable limestone layer called caliche.

C HORIZON — Zone of bedrock weathering.

Arid soils are not as thick as those in warm, high-rainfall environments.

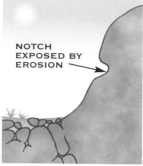

NOTCH FORMING

NOTCH EXPOSED BY EROSION

BEDROCK

Development of paleosoil notches in Joshua Tree's granite.

abrasion, but in many places tafoni pockets are aligned parallel to the soil-outcrop contact, implying that they may have originated beneath the soil in a manner similar to the forming of notches. The subsoil development of tafoni is probably a two-stage process. In the first stage, localized concentrations of acids associated with plant decay and other biological soil

wearing back and rounding off higher up on the cliff face cannot keep pace with the undercutting at the base.

Inselberg west of Indian Cove Group Campsite showing ancient subsoil notching, with rock-varnish-coated surfaces above and nonvarnished surfaces below the notch. Such exposures reveal the lowering of soil levels in recent geologic time, probably within the last 20,000 years.

Large scale tafoni in granite. It is unclear why some tafoni occur in sets in some places but as isolated features in others. Note the variation in sizes and depths of the pits, another geological puzzle.

HONEYCOMBS

Concave hollows and pits, called tafoni, a Corsican term for honeycomb structures, are common on rock surfaces in Joshua Tree granites. Although tafoni are rather common phenomena, their origin is not clearly understood. In some cases, tafoni are considered to be a product of wind

processes cause intense weathering at points in adjoining subterranean bedrock. This is probably assisted by periodic wetting and drying of the soil. The second step is the erosion of the soil along the base of rock faces that exposes the chemically weathered holes. Because of lower evaporation rates in the hollows and pits once they are exposed, they weather more rapidly than the surrounding rock, gradually enlarging and sometimes merging into larger pits.

At Joshua Tree, tafoni are restricted

Skull Rock is an especially good example of tafoni and also shows how widely spaced joints control the development of landforms in granitic rocks.

mainly to granitic rocks. The darker gneiss of the park weathers and breaks down differently than granite owing to its different mineral composition and the rock's platy, layered structure that greatly accelerates weathering processes. Where some granite plutons may stand up in bold, rounded outcrops, gneiss tends to form gentler slopes dissected by rugged stream drainages. As you visit the park, take time to notice the differences in the topography created by these two rock types. Gneiss makes up almost all of the darker highlands and ridges in the western portion of the park in contrast to the steeper, more spectacular outcroppings of lighter-colored granite in the central portion of the park.

VENTIFACTS

Erosion is any process that removes fragments of bedrock, other rock materials, or soils from their place of origin. Sand dunes, which cover only 5 percent of the arid lands in the southwestern United States, are a spectacular product of erosion

and deposition, forming where wind sweeping across many square miles of land picks up large amounts of finely fragmented rock grains and blows them into piles. In places, the wind blows sand grains across the bare rock surfaces, abrading and sculpting the rock into streaked, streamlined shapes. Such wind-sculpted rocks are called ventifacts. Spectacular ventifacts may be seen in places atop the lava mesas and bluffs where Old Dale Road reaches the northern edge of Pinto Basin. In this area, persistent seasonal winds blow across a broad pass in the Pinto Mountains.

It is water, more than wind, that remains the greater agent of erosion in arid regions. A huge "gully-washer," or flash

Wind-fluted ventifact.

Wind-sculptured ventifacts resting on desert pavement on the ridge along the northern edge of the Pinto Basin, northwest of Mission Well. Pinto Mountains in the distance.

Intrusive contact between the White Tank monzogranite (rugged, light-colored outcrops on the left) and the Queen Mountain monzogranite (dark, less rugged hills on the right) in the Wonderland of Rocks area.

flood, can reconfigure the scenery dramatically within a matter of minutes.

THE ROLE OF CATASTROPHES

When geology was being formulated as a new science in the late eighteenth century, one of the original tenets was that ordinary processes acting over long spans of time can wholly alter the appearance of a landscape. This is known as the Principle of Uniformitarianism, the idea that the processes we now see operating on the earth's surface have occurred more or less constantly throughout history, shaping the world as we see it by gradual, incremental change. While substantially true, not all turns out to be as it once seemed to the founders of geology. Many early geologists criticized the traditional biblical notion of a world born in the Creation and shaped by single catastrophe, Noah's Flood. We now know that "catastrophes" must be included among the ordinary processes that shape the earth's surface. An earthquake may rumble through, triggering rock falls and landslides, changing the shapes of canyon walls and hillsides for many centuries.

CLIMATE CHANGE AND THE JOSHUA TREE LANDSCAPE

Another early geological notion held that the continental configuration and broad environment of the earth had remained essentially the same since the planet first formed. The idea that continents could shift and bump into one another was widely resisted by the geological community until the irrefutable evidence of plate tectonics emerged in the late 1960s. It is not that the early geologists were unintelligent; far from it. They were being properly conservative about interpreting what they knew about the world in light of the knowledge of the time. We know much more today, thanks to new technologies that enable us to study the world more thoroughly.

Hence, many early geologists believed deserts' characteristic landforms developed from weathering and erosion under unchanging arid conditions. In fact, the weathering and erosional processes presently active in the arid regions of the western United States are not the primary cause of the spectacular sculpturing of the rocks we see in Joshua Tree National Park, Death Valley, and the Mojave Desert. The present landscape is essentially a collection of features inherited from much earlier times. Actually, the desert landscape may be thought of as a fossil landscape. Consider Fortynine Palms Canyon. Such a deep, steep-walled canyon could not have formed in the present rainfall regime. It formed when the region received much greater precipitation than at present, when evaporation was less, and the average temperature was several degrees cooler.

TRANSFORMATION FROM SAVANNA TO DESERT

Climatic conditions during late Tertiary and Pleistocene times (from approximately 25 million to 10,000 years ago) were quite different than today, and the role of the former climate was critical in the development of today's desert landscape. The present climate of the western deserts is relatively new. Around 25 million years ago the Joshua Tree landscape resembled an African grassland savanna with scattered trees and shrubs and laced with streams and water holes that provided water year round to a host of large, browsing mammals — all now extinct — including ancestral camels, horses, lions, and antelopes. (The fossils of many of these animals have been recovered from sedimentary strata of the Hector Formation in the Cady Mountains, the Barstow Formation in Rainbow Basin near Fort Irwin, and elsewhere in the Mojave Desert.) At the time, there were no Transverse Ranges between the Joshua Tree region and the coast. One might have had only to cross low-lying hills, maybe skirting a volcanic cone or two, in order to reach the coast, which in places was many miles inland from its present position.

Botanical evidence indicates that progressive deterioration of vegetation began taking place throughout the Mojave Desert region from approximately 24 million to 1.6 million years ago. The most important long-term cause for this climate change was the uplift of young mountain ranges between the region of the park and the ocean. Collision along the east-west stretch of the San Andreas Fault raised the San Gabriel Mountains to moderate relief by about seven million years ago during a mountain-building epoch known as the Pasadenan Orogeny. But the major uplift of the range has occurred within only the past five million years. Uplift of the San Bernardino Mountains is even more recent. About three million years ago, the highlands around Big Bear Lake and Lake Arrowhead lay at the elevation of the neighboring Ontario Plain, 1,000 to 1,500 feet (300 to 400 m) above sea level. The high country of the San Bernardino Range, with elevations of 6,000 to 7,000 feet (1,700 to 2,000 m) above sea level, is still fairly level, although rolling, because there has been insufficient time since its uplift to erode the range into steep, rugged mountains like the San Gabriels to the west. (The massif of Mount San Gorgonio, 11,700 feet or 3,750 m high, the tallest peak in the San Bernardino Range, has a geologic history separate from that of the main range of the San Bernardinos). Coincident with the uplift of the Transverse Ranges was the uplifting of the Sierra Nevada to the north, all of which combined to hinder the passage of storms and greatly reduce rainfall east of these mountains. It is the uplift of these ranges that marks the birth of the desert around Joshua Tree.

ICE AGES

The cyclic pattern of climate changes during the ice ages that have gripped the earth over the past two million years has been superposed on these long-term tectonic changes. During each of the ice ages, the earth was much colder than at present and today's desert regions were wetter, and generally had a stable soil cover and abundant vegetation. In fact, today's relatively warm climate is thought to be an epoch between ice ages. Such interglacial epochs last only 10,000 to 35,000 years and are separated by intervening glacial epochs of perhaps 100,000 to 250,000 years. We are about 11,000 years into the current interglacial epoch, which is called the Holocene. In the context of geology, the next ice age looms just over the horizon. (Some climatologists believe that global warming, due to a variety of ocean/land/atmospheric interactions induced by human activity, could hasten the arrival of this event.) The last ice age reached its frigid climax about 20,000 years ago. The earth's climate warmed hesitatingly until about 11,000 years ago at which time it suddenly warmed to present temperatures, a 9°F (5°C) increase in worldwide average temperature. About 8,500 to 5,000 years ago, the earth's climate was actually much warmer than at present. Since then cooling has taken place, but during this last interval the temperature fluctuations were erratic. Beginning about A.D. 1500 and lasting until about 1900 (or 1930 accord-

- ABRUPT CHANGES IN SLOPE AT THE CONTACTS OF DIFFERENT ROCK TYPES.

- ABRUPT TRANSITIONS IN SLOPE WHERE HILLSIDES JOIN VALLEY FLOORS.

- JAGGED SUMMITS, NOT SMOOTHLY ROUNDED AS IN HUMID REGIONS.

- STEEP SLOPES THAT REMAIN STEEP, EVEN ON WIDE DESERT PLAINS WHERE THERE ARE ONLY ISOLATED BUTTES REMAINING AFTER A LONG EPISODE OF EROSION AND REMOVAL OF GREAT VOLUMES OF ROCK.

- ALLUVIAL FANS, SEDIMENT DEPOSITED AT THE MOUTHS OF CANYONS.

- BAJADAS, BROAD, SLOPING APRONS OF ROCK DEBRIS FORMED BY LATERAL COALESCENCE OF SEVERAL ALLUVIAL FANS.

- PLAYAS, UNDRAINED DESERT BASINS THAT MAY CONTAIN WATER ONLY DURING THE RAINY SEASON.

- ARROYOS OR WASHES, EPHEMERAL OR INTERMITTENT STREAM COURSES THAT MAY CONTAIN WATER ONLY A FEW HOURS OR PERHAPS A FEW DAYS EACH YEAR DURING THE RAINY SEASON.

- PEDIMENTS, PLANAR, ROCK-CUT, GENTLY SLOPING BEDROCK SURFACES CARVED AT THE BASE OF DESERT MOUNTAINS; THEIR LOWER MARGINS MAY MERGE WITH BAJADAS.

- INSELBERGS, ISOLATED, STEEP-SIDED RESIDUAL BEDROCK KNOBS THAT RISE ABRUPTLY FROM PEDIMENTS, LIKE ISLANDS IN THE SEA (INSEL IS ISLAND IN GERMAN).

- BOLSONS, BASINS OF INTERNAL DRAINAGE SURROUNDED BY BAJADA SLOPES.

- BROAD DESERT VALLEYS, LIKE BOLSONS, BUT WITH DRY OUTLETS TO OTHER VALLEYS OR STREAMS, SUCH AS THE COLORADO RIVER.

ing to some authorities), the earth was subjected to atmospheric conditions so cool that a mere 2.7 to 3.6°F (1.5 to 2°C) drop in average temperature would have returned us to ice-age temperatures; this period is known as the Little Ice Age.

WARMING UP AND DRYING OUT

Sudden warming at the end of ice ages is responsible for creating most of the unique landforms, other than basins and ranges, that people so readily associate with the southern California desert. Some geologists believe, however, that earlier regional drying out during uplift of the coastal mountains also contributed to forming the features seen in the present-day landscape.

A key aspect of a drying climate is that it causes a corresponding change in the density of plant cover, leading to increasingly larger areas of soil and loose rock unprotected by vegetation. Thus, the potential for the land to erode and the amount of material available for running water and wind to pick up and transport as sediment increases. At the same time, the rate of new soil formation due to weathering and biological activity decreases. As a result, the rate of erosion soon exceeds the rate of soil formation, and erosion strips the land surface, especially hill slopes, of soil cover.

How Low Can It Go?
Finding Base Level

The fate of the lost soil cover, which instantaneously becomes sediment as it washes downslope, is also greatly influenced by the climate.

The lowest elevation to which running streams can erode the land is called base level. This corresponds to the lowest elevation that stream waters can reach. In most places around the world, this is sea level.

In fact, many geologists refer to sea level as the ultimate base level for streams and rivers. It is not possible for running water to continue downcutting a valley floor below a base level.

In arid areas, however, several factors operate to prevent water from washing sediment all the way to the sea. Insufficient precipitation is the most obvious factor. This, combined with high evaporation rates and high rates of groundwater infiltration, prevents desert streams from flowing either very long or very far. Heavy winter rains in today's southern California desert are not likely to fill the bottoms of the ancient ice-age lakes for more than a few weeks at a time.

Basins

Another factor is rapid tectonic activity. Blocks of faulted crust create an extremely irregular topography of mountain ranges and intervening basins. The basins are not usually linked through low passes that would permit water to flow from one basin to the other. Instead, each basin serves as a giant receptacle, a local base level, for sediment washed from short streams that drain immediately adjacent mountains. Owens and Death Valleys and the Salton Trough are examples of such basins. In a more humid climate, each

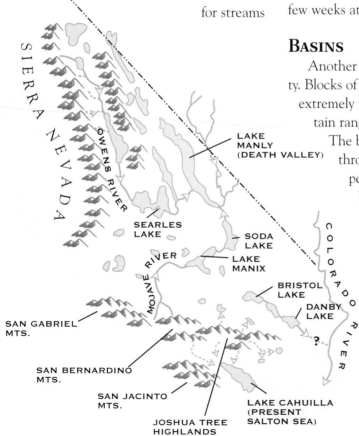

Ice age lakes of the southeastern California deserts. (Modified from Blackwelder, 1954.)

basin might become a large lake, allowing water to spill out from one to another, eventually to reach the sea. Erosion would break down the bedrock sills between the basins, smoothing out a coherent path for running water so that a string of originally isolated basins would become a single long, wide valley. Such a condition is called an integrated drainage system; all streams and rivers linked together in a shared watershed. Deserts, especially those in tectonically active areas, characteristically have nonintegrated drainages, with huge sediment accumulations that in wetter climates would be removed by running water. They also have wide, generally elevated areas of exposed bedrock, stripped bare by erosion.

During periods of climate fluctuations, regions can alternate between having integrated drainage during moist periods and nonintegrated drainage during dry periods. During the periodic ice ages, runoff water, originating by the melting from heavy snow packs and from glacial ice in the Sierra Nevada and San Bernardino Mountains, extended the lengths of the Owens and Mojave Rivers across the desert of southern California. Where these rivers entered basins, the water filled them to overflowing, resulting in linking up adjoining basins. For example, the ancestral Owens River connected a chain of lakes extending from Mono Lake to Death Valley, which is a valley so large that it could not be filled; evaporation ultimately removed the water

as fast as it flowed in. At one time, the Mojave River also flowed north into Death Valley forming Soda Lake and Silver Lake along the way, both of which have since completely evaporated.

PLAYAS

The Spanish word for beach, *playa,* also refers to dry ice-age lakebeds throughout the California desert. When a lake dries up, it leaves behind beds of silt, clay, and minerals such as halite, borates, and gypsum that can only form by evaporation of saline water. Some of these evaporite deposits are commercially valuable. Early mining of salts from playas helped support the region's gold mining. Chlorine obtained from halite was used in the milling process that separated the gold from its ore. Even today, continued mining of the ice-age playas produces important mineral products for use in water treatment, cleansing agents, in manufacturing acids, and for other products.

The Geology Tour Road within Pleasant Valley crosses one small, easily accessible playa in Joshua Tree National Park. Fine clays floor the playa, which is partly overgrown and inconspicuous.

A string of playas, including Deadman and Dale, received the discharge of streams flowing northward out of the park during the latest ice age. Deadman Playa, west of the Twentynine Palms Marine Corps Air Ground Combat Center, and Dale Dry Lake, north of Highway 62, 20

Bajada at the base of the Pinto Mountains as seen from the Turkey Flats backcountry registration board on Pinto Basin Road.

miles (32 km) east of Twentynine Palms, lie within fault-bounded basins with bedrock floors buried under thousands of feet of sediment. Were it not for the erosion of surrounding mountain ranges and consequent sedimentary infilling, the surface of the entire region would be staggeringly rugged.

ALLUVIAL FANS

Alluvium is sediment that has been deposited by streams on dry land; it has not accumulated in an ocean or lake. Alluvial fans are broad sediment piles built up at the mouths of canyons. They may merge together to form vast alluvial slopes called *bajadas,* a Spanish word roughly translating as "descent." Some geologists believe that the development of alluvial fans in California's desert is a two-stage process that is activated whenever climate suddenly becomes more arid. Accelerated weathering during more temperate ice-age times produced soil-mantled slopes in mountain areas. Grasses, pinyon, juniper, and perhaps chaparral anchored the soil cover on mountain slopes.

Stage 1. When an ice age ends, the subsequent dry conditions kill off many plants, thus exposing the soil, which storms can then erode and wash away. Runoff, too, increases because of the loss of the protective plant cover. Consequently, streams that had formerly been comfortably maintaining equilibrium in a less arid climate abruptly find themselves transporting enormous volumes of newly loosened material because of the climate change. Given the reduced but still highly erosive volume of water moving through streams and the rapid dissipation of that water in the basins and valleys below, the streams simply dump the sediment at the foot of each mountain canyon, building up huge alluvial fans. Stage 1 gradually passes into Stage 2 as the sediment supply diminishes from mountain slopes above; and Stage 2 redistributes the sediment that accumulates during Stage 1.

Stage 2. As the supply of soil and grus in the highlands is stripped off and carried away, a strikingly rough mountain landscape emerges resembling that of today. Whenever rain falls at this stage, however, there is little loose material remaining for it to remove from the mountainsides. The water racing down the canyons toward the fans below has the capacity to carry much more sediment than is available, and thus has extra energy to expend. It begins eroding the alluvial fans that had been deposited not long before, creating huge trenches at the heads of the fans. In the lower reaches of the alluvial fans, the dissipating flood waters lose their energy and redeposit the sediment, building out the bases of the fans even as the upslope fan heads erode downward.

We can recognize the difference in ages of the older Stage-1 fans and the younger, freshly deposited Stage-2 fans not only by looking for the presence of fanhead trenches but also by observing the colors of the fans from a distance. Boulders on older fans generally have a darker patina resulting from rock varnish, a thin coating of iron- and manganese-rich mineral material.

The most spectacular alluvial fans to be seen in the Joshua Tree area actually do not lie within the park boundary. As one leaves the park through the Cottonwood (southeast) entrance, the view across the valley toward the Orocopia Mountains is dominated by an enormous bajada that has

Three stages of rock varnish development on granite.

undergone extensive fanhead trenching. Some arroyo trenches continue to the base of the bajada, showing that flash flooding in recent geological times has begun transporting sediment away from the bajada

DEVELOPMENT AND GROWTH OF ALLUVIAL FANS IN CALIFORNIA DESERTS

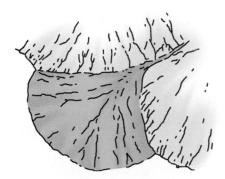

STAGE 1. Growth of older fan when stream is transporting a heavy sediment load.

STAGE 2. Growth of younger fan and the cutting of a fanhead trench due to erosion by a sediment-starved stream.

ROCK VARNISH AND PICTURES IN STONE

MANY DESERT ROCKS HAVE A BROWN-BLACK OR REDDISH-BROWN COATING. THE DARKER "VARNISH" CONTAINS MANGANESE THAT ORIGINATES FROM FINE ATMOSPHERIC DUST SET IN PLACE BY MICROORGANISMS AFTER IT SETTLES ON EXPOSED ROCK SURFACES. THE REDDISH-BROWN IRON OXIDES ORIGINATE BY CHEMICAL WEATHERING OF THE BURIED PARTS OF COBBLES AND BOULDERS IN SHALLOW GROUND.

Petroglyphs etched through rock varnish.

ALTHOUGH COMMONLY IDENTIFIED WITH DESERT AREAS, ROCK VARNISH FORMS IN A VARIETY OF CLIMATES. WE SIMPLY AREN'T USED TO SEEING IT IN MORE HUMID REGIONS BECAUSE LESS ROCK IS EXPOSED, AND FREQUENT RAINFALL KEEPS DOWN DUST AND CLEANS ROCK SURFACES. EARLY NATIVES AND LATER IMMIGRANTS MADE USE OF VARNISHED ROCKS TO PRODUCE SYMBOLS, ART, AND PERHAPS MAPS BY ETCHING AWAY THE DARK COATINGS TO EXPOSE THE FRESH LIGHT-COLORED ROCK BENEATH. MANY OLDER PETROGLYPHS MAY HAVE A GREATER BUILDUP OF VARNISH AND ARE SOMEWHAT DARKER THAN YOUNGER ONES.

IN 1977, TWO RESEARCHERS WERE ABLE TO DETERMINE AN AGE OF 9,100 YEARS FOR PETROGLYPHS IN THE SALTON SEA AREA. STUDIES INDICATE THAT AFTER 100,000 YEARS, TYPICAL VARNISH WILL BE ABOUT TWO-THIRDS AS DARK AS IT CAN GET, WITH AN ADDITIONAL HALF-MILLION YEARS REQUIRED FOR THE LAST ONE-THIRD OF THE DARKENING. CONSEQUENTLY, PETROGLYPHS MAY BE AMONG THE MOST LONG-LASTING TRACES OF HUMANKIND.

altogether, flushing it toward the nearby Salton Trough, which serves as the local base level for the southern part of the park. Smaller alluvial fans form at the mouths of some canyons along the northern and southern fringes of the Pinto Basin. Much larger fans are found at the base of the Coxcomb Mountains at the eastern end of the park.

PEDIMENTS

Pediments are gently sloping exposed bedrock surfaces that extend outward and away from the base of desert mountain ranges. They are a curious desert landform, typical of the southwestern United States and many other desert areas of the world. Superficially, pediments resemble bajadas (depositional features) but pediments are rock-cut features that are eroded on bedrock or hardened alluvium.

Some investigators consider pediments the only true desert landform whose origin can be attributed solely to the arid conditions operating at present. Others regard pediments as features that have developed in a sequential manner over a long period. The following explanation, a three-stage process illustrated in the accompanying diagram, is one that we believe is at least close to being true.

Stage 1. Weathering and erosion of a mountain front during temperate semiarid to subhumid times causes the mountain front to retreat.

Stage 2. At the base of the retreating

Pediment at the base of the Eagle Mountains viewed from the Mastodon Peak Trail near Cottonwood Campground.

front, a layer of sediment is left behind, overlying a bedrock surface that represents the part of the mountain front that was too deep to weaken and erode. This bedrock surface, now buried by alluvium and sloping gently away from the retreating mountain front, will eventually become the pediment.

Stage 3. The climate changes to that of a desert. In the new climatic regime, the erosion of soils and the thinning and disappearance of vegetation promote flash floods and soil erosion during short but intensive rains. Consequently, the veneer of sediment covering the bedrock surface

that remained when the hill slopes retreated in less arid times is stripped off, exposing the bedrock pediment surface.

INSELBERGS AND BOULDER MANTLES

Inselbergs are isolated, steep-sided bedrock knobs that rise abruptly from pediments but sometimes are surrounded by alluvium. They are distinctive features of the Joshua Tree desert landscape for which there are different ideas of origin. Their beginnings in the Mojave region extends back as far as seven to nine million years, perhaps longer, when the landscape was one of smooth, rolling hills covered with a mantle of well-vegetated soil rather than the raw, rugged bedrock slopes that we see today. The climate and the amount of plant cover must have been somewhat similar to that of today's mountains in western Riverside and San Diego Counties. The hills and ridges contained cores of relatively unjointed, massive granite, whereas the intervening valleys were developed in areas of more intensively jointed, easily weathered and eroded rock. These less arid times

THE ORIGIN OF PEDIMENTS

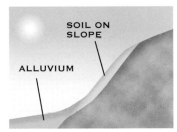

SOIL ON SLOPE

ALLUVIUM

STAGE 1. Early mountain front retreating during time of semiarid to subhumid climate.

STAGE 2. Continued retreat during semiarid to subhumid climate; future pediment beginning to form.

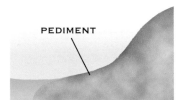

PEDIMENT

STAGE 3. After climate has become arid, flash floods and sheet wash sweep off the veneer of sediment to reveal the pediment.

were periods during which more soil formed than was eroded. As the climate dried, vegetation receded and erosion increased, stripping the residual soils from the steeper hillsides. Remaining were granite boulders too heavy for wind or water to transport, boulders that formerly had been subsurface joint blocks in the C horizon, rounded out and isolated by chemical decomposition along the joint planes. Today these residual C-horizon stones form boulder-mantled slopes, good examples of which may be seen along the road between the town of Joshua Tree and Hidden Valley Campground.

In some places, weathering and erosion have completely removed all but the resistant bedrock cores of the ancient hills, leaving bold, craggy inselberg knobs. Unlike exfoliation domes, inselbergs are not rounded and they tend to be smaller features. They form spectacular prominences at Hidden Valley, Cap Rock, Jumbo Rocks, and along the Geology Tour Road. Inselbergs usually consist of

Partially boulder-mantled slope along Park Road between Hidden Valley and the west entrance to the park.

granite, only rarely of gneiss, since it weathers more completely than granite.

Evidence for this origin of inselberg and boulder-mantled slopes comes from Black Mountain near State Highway 247, about 22 miles (33 km) west-northwest of Twentynine Palms. Here reddish iron-oxide and calcite-rich soil and rounded boulders have been preserved beneath basalt lava flows with radiometric ages of 6.9 to 9.3 million years. Similar reddish soils form

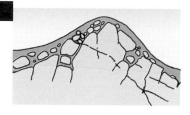

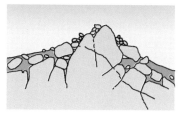

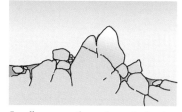

Inselbergs are the resistant bedrock cores of ancient hills.

The intrusive contact between the ancient gneiss and the younger White Tank monzogranite on the western flank of Ryan Mountain.

54

today in warm semiarid regions with heavy plant cover and average annual rainfall exceeding ten inches (25 cm). Continuity between these buried relict soils and associated debris with nearby boulder-mantled slopes clearly establishes the boulder mantle as a relict feature inherited from a former time of deep weathering, most likely about nine million years ago in the late Tertiary period. Presumably, the boulder mantles on slopes in Joshua Tree are remnant core-stones of the same age as those embedded in the the ancient soil beneath the lavas at Black Mountain.

WIDE VALLEYS AND BASINS

Wide valleys and basins floored with miles and miles of alluvium are spectacular aspects of the Joshua Tree landscape. The presence of these extensive alluvial plains is largely a testament to the fact that with the drying out of the Joshua Tree climate, the rather suddenly eroded soil and sediment derived from the surrounding hill and mountainsides could not be transported out of the region by running water. The alluvium filled and clogged what formerly had been a network of deeper, narrower valleys and canyons that are now flat-floored and partly or completely buried.

By strolling along any of the innumerable desert washes in the park, we can appreciate, on a small scale, this disparity between sediment supply and the ability of streams to transport it under present

Late Miocene basalt flows (6.9 – 9.3 Ma) at the crest of Black Mountain on the east side of State Highway 247 north of Yucca Valley at Pipe Springs Road. (Age data from Morton, 1993.)

55

DEVELOPMENT OF GEOLOGIC RELATIONSHIPS AT BLACK MOUNTAIN

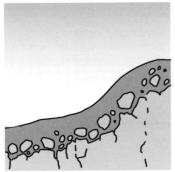

Thick soil mantle on weathered granite about ten million years ago.

Immediately after the episode of volcanism about eight million years ago.

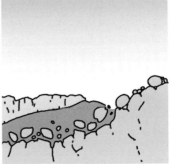

Today the ancient soil is protected from erosion by the remnant of the old basalt flow and the boulder-mantled slope of core-stones.

conditions. Except in steep highland areas, the bottoms of most washes are covered with sand, occasional gravel patches, and a few boulders. Typically, the floors of these sandy washes are wide. In regions with abundant rainfall where clear, running water might be observed year round, sand has been swept downstream, and the beds tend to be so narrow and rocky that it is difficult to find steady footing.

DUNES

Upon evaporation of the ice-age lakes, the fine sediment in their beds quickly blew away and much of it accumulated downwind in large dunes. Some dunes

In humid regions, the vegetation on hillslopes guarantees that there will be little runoff into streams. Trapped by vegetation, leaf litter, etc., water slowly percolates into the ground. Humid areas generally lack intensive erosion. Extensive products of weathering, in the form of soil and grus, remain on the land at or near where they formed.

The lack of vegetation in deserts means that there are widespread areas of rocky outcrops stripped bare of soil. When it does rain, runoff is more intensive and slope erosion tends to be intensive. Because of stream flow, boulders, grus, and soil tend to clog stream beds and fill valley floors, creating wide, sediment-filled valleys and arroyos.

became stabilized by cross winds blowing over the irregular land. Some acquired mantles of vegetation as sand supply diminished. Dunes most probably represent the collective deposits of many events of lake evaporation over the past few million years, with a significant amount of sand contributed from the last great evaporation 10,000 to 20,000 years ago.

The best sand dunes in the park are in the Pinto Basin, not far from the Cholla Cactus Garden. The source of this sand was a wide complex of integrated, eastward-draining washes in the center of the basin. The Pinto Basin, despite its name, has an outlet to the southeast that in times past allowed its runoff waters to reach Palen Dry Lake east of Desert Center; therefore, an ice-age lake never formed here. The Pinto Basin dunes field is quite small compared to those in the California desert that received sand from the great Pleistocene lakes and playas. Moreover, the sand is not as thick as it appears from a distance, being underlain and anchored by a low ridge of bedrock that has uplifted along a strand of the Blue Cut Fault.

Sand dunes form where turbulence reduces the carrying capacity of the wind and sediment accumulates against hills, rough spots, even stones or brush in the landscape. The sand itself acts as a barrier and promotes accumulation of additional sand. Dunes have a characteristic profile, sloping gradually upward on the side that catches the sand, then steeply downward on the downwind side. The downwind slope is at the angle of repose, the steepest angle at which loose sediment can rest without sliding downslope, 33 degrees for loose, dry sand.

DESERT PAVEMENT

Desert pavement consists of bits of gravel and pebbles that are closely spaced on the desert floor. Commonly, pavements are darkly coated with rock varnish, although some rock types, such as volcanic tuff and limestone, never acquire varnish because of the active chemical weathering taking place on their surfaces. Some pavements, made up of rock fragments from multiple sources, consist of pieces of varying size but other pavements are well sorted and the surface crudely resembles a mosaic floor. The uniform size distribution suggests breakdown of larger rocks by mechanical weathering along incipient cracks, by wedging of salt or gypsum grains that were carried by the wind from playa lakes, freeze-thaw cycling, and solar heating. A layer of soft, porous silt as much as several inches thick underlies most pavements. For most of the twentieth century, geologists interpreted this unusual surface as formed by some combination of intense runoff during rainstorms, and strong winds blowing across the desert floor. These actions were presumed to erode the fine particles to leave behind a surface armor of coarse-grained fragments. Indeed, some of the best desert pavements observed in

The rock-hammer scratch reveals that desert pavement stones are underlain at shallow depth by powdery soil. Notice the uniform size of the pavement stones, which indicates that they are of great age.

Joshua Tree are closely associated with ventifacts.

Studies raise doubt about an origin by wind and runoff erosion by showing that the basal layer of soft silt has originated by the accumulation of dust beneath the evolving pavement. This layer can be as much as several inches thick and includes scattered air pockets. The wind-borne dust that has settled on the surface works downward between the pebbles, perhaps aided by infiltrating rainwater. Thus, the pavements are lifted from their original position as silt and dust accumulate below them. The process is not uniform, however, leaving the many pores that are characteristic of soils underlying pavements.

Whatever their origin, we know that desert pavements are extremely fragile surfaces and take a long time, perhaps as much as 100,000 years, to fully form. Driving vehicles across pavements can leave scars that persist for decades or centuries. The tracks of armored military vehicles that scarred Mojave Desert pavements in 1943 and 1964 are still clearly evident. Many centuries before the arrival of immigrants, American Indians created giant human and animal figures, called intaglios, still obvious in pavements along the Colorado River, by selectively stripping pavements of their stones to expose the light-colored soils underneath.

HUMANITY — A NEW FORCE FOR GEOLOGIC CHANGE

Geomorphologists, geologists who study the evolution of landscapes, have learned much by simply applying common sense observation to the desert landscape, but there is a world of information still to be discovered. Much that we think we understand today eventually may be refined, corrected, and augmented. The field of geomorphology is currently in full blossom. Its ultimate contribution, to help us usefully comprehend our place in Earth's long history, is yet to be realized. Its importance increases in time, given a dawning realization that humans themselves have become major agents of geological change. One of the great values of a place like Joshua Tree National Park is that it provides a reminder of natural being and an index of nature's response to our increasingly artificial world.

ADDITIONAL READING & REFERENCES

Axelrod, D.I., "Evolution of the macro-Tertiary geoflora," Botanical Review 24, no. 7 (1958): 433–509.

Barth, A.P.; Tosdal, R.M.; Wooden, J.L.; and Howard, K.A., "Triassic plutonism in southern California: Southward younging of an arc initiation along a truncated continental margin," Tectonics 16, no. 2 (1997): 290–304.

Blackwelder, E., "Pleistocene lakes and drainages in the Mojave region, southern California," in R.H. Jahns, editor, The Geology of Southern California, Bulletin 170 (1954), California Division of Mines and Geology: 35–40.

Blythe, Ann E.; Burbank, D.W.; Farley, K.A.; Fielding, E.J., "Structural and topographic evolution of the central Transverse Ranges, California, from apatite fission-track, (U-Th)/He and digital elevation model analyses," Basin Research 12 (2000): 97–114.

Borg, S.C., and DePaolo, D., "Laurentia, Australia, and Antarctica as a late Proterozoic supercontinent," Geology 22 (1994): 307–310.

Bortugno, E.J., and Spittler, T.E., "Geologic map of the San Bernardino Quadrangle," map scale 1:250,000, California Division of Mines and Geology, 1986.

Brand, J.H., and Anderson, J.L., "Mesozoic alkalic monzonites and peraluminous adamelites of the Joshua Tree National Monument, southern California" [abstract], Geological Society of America Abstracts with Programs 14, no. 4 (1982): 151–152.

Broecker, Wallace S., and Liu, Tanzhuo, "Rock varnish: Recorder of desert wetness?" GSA Today 11, no. 8 (2001): 4–10.

Brookfield, M.E., "Neoproterozoic Laurentia–Australia fit," Geology 22 (1993)

Bull, William B., Geomorphic Responses to Climatic Change. New York: Oxford University Press, 1991.

Candela, P.A., "A review of shallow, ore-related granites: Textures, volatiles, and ore metals," Journal of Petrology 38, no.12 (1997): 1619–1633.

Dibblee, T.W., Jr., "Geologic map of the Joshua Tree Quadrangle, San Bernardino and Riverside Counties, California," U.S. Geological Survey Miscellaneous Geologic Investigations Map I-516, 1967.

_____, "Geologic map of the Twentynine Palms Quadrangle, San Bernardino and Riverside Counties, California," U.S. Geological Survey Miscellaneous Geologic Investigations Map I-561, 1968b.

Dorn, R.I., and Oberlander, T.M., "Microbial origin of desert varnish," Science 213, no. 11 September (1981): 1245–1247.

Hope, Roger A., "The Blue Cut fault, southeastern California," U.S. Geological Survey Professional Paper 650-D (1969): 116–121.

Hopson, R. Forrest, "Quaternary geology and neotectonics of the Pinto Mountain fault, Mojave Desert, southern California," California Geology 51, no. 6, (November–December 1998): 3–13.

Hughes, R.O., III; Evenson, E.G.; Gosse, J.C.; and Harrington, C., "Tafoni, genesis in arid climates; paleoclimatological implications" [abstract], Abstracts with Programs, Geological Society of America 30th Annual Northeastern Sectional meeting (1995): 56.

Karlstrom, K.E.; Harlan, S.S.; Williams, M.L.; McClelland, J.; Geissman, J.W.; and Åhall, K.I., "Refining Rodinia: Geologic evidence for the Australia–western U.S. connection in the Proterozoic," GSA Today 9, no. 10 (1999): 1–7, 683–686.

Liu, Tanzhuo, and Broecker, Wallace S., "How fast does rock varnish grow?" Geology 28, no. 2 (2000): 183–186.

_____, and Dorn, R.I., "Understanding the spatial arability of environmental change in the dry lands with rock varnish microlaminations," Annals of the Association of American Geographers 86, no. 2 (1996): 187–212.

McFadden, L.D.; Wells, S.G.; and Jercinovich, J.L., "Influences of eolian and pedogenic processes on the origin of evolution of desert pavements," Geology 15 (1987): 504–508.

_____, Epps, M.C.; Wells, S.G.; and Gillespie, A.R., "The evolution of desert piedmont surfaces: Studies of the origin of desert pavements and soil," Geological Society of America Abstracts with Programs 32, no. 7 (2000): A-222.

Morton, D.M., cited in Reynolds, R.E.; Buising, A.V.; and Beratan, K.K., "The 1992 Mojave Desert Quaternary Research Center Trip," in Reynolds, R.E., editor, Old routes to the Colorado. Redlands, California: San Bernardino County Museum Association, Special Publication 92-1 (1985): 5–27.

Mueller, J.E., and Twidale, C.R., "Geomorphic development of the City of Rocks, Grant County, New Mexico," New Mexico Geology 10, no. 4 (November 1988): 73–79.

Oberlander, T.M., "Morphogenesis of granite boulder slopes in the Mojave Desert, California," Journal of Geology 80, no. 12 (1972): 1–20.

_____, and Dorn, R.I., "Microbial origin of desert varnish," Science 213 (1981): 1245–1247.

Parker, Jeffrey, "Late Pleistocene tufa near Cottonwood Spring, Joshua Tree National Park," senior thesis, Pomona College, 2001.

Powell, R.E., "Crystalline basement terranes in the southeastern Transverse Ranges, California," in Cooper, J.D., editor, "Geologic excursions in the Transverse Ranges: Geological Society of America Cordilleran Section," 78th annual meeting, Anaheim, California (1982): 109–136.

Sadler, Peter M., "The Santa Ana basin of the central San Bernardino Mountains: Evidence of the timing of uplift and strike slip relative to the San Gabriel Mountains," in Powell,

R.E.; Weldon, R.J., II; and Matti, J.C.; editors, "The San Andreas Fault System: Displacement, palinspastic reconstruction, and geologic evolution," Boulder, Colorado, Geological Society of America Memoir 178 (1993): 307–321.

Schoenherr, Allan, A Natural History of California. Berkeley: University of California Press, 1992.

Spaulding, W.G., and Graumlich, L.J., "The last pluvial climatic episodes in the deserts of southwestern North America," Nature 320 (1986): 441–444.

Turner, W.G., and Reynolds, Robert, "Dating the Salton Sea petroglyphs," Science News 111, no. 9 (February 26, 1977): 138.

Twidale, C.R., Granite landforms. Amsterdam: Elsivier, 1982.

Williams, P.L.; Sykes, L.R.; Nicholson, C.R.; and Seeber, L., "Seismotectonics of the easternmost Transverse Ranges, California: Relevance for seismic potential of the southern San Andreas fault," Tectonics 9 (1990): 185–202.

Wilshire, H.G., and Reneau, S.L., "Geomorphic surfaces and underlying deposits of the Mojave Mountains piedmont, Lower Colorado River, Arizona," Zeitschrift für Geomorphologie 36, no. 2 (1992): 207–226.

Wooden, J.L.; Tosdal, R.M.; Howard, K.A.; Powell, R.E.; Matti, J.C.; and Barth, A.P., "Mesozoic intrusive history of parts of the eastern Transverse Ranges, California, preliminary U-Pb zircon results" [abstract], Geological Society of America Abstracts with Programs 26, no. 2 (1994): A104–105.

GLOSSARY

Alluvial fan: a fan-shaped mass of rock debris formed at the mouth of a canyon in an arid region

Alluvium: sediment that has been deposited on land by running water

Andesite: a volcanic rock similar to basalt but typically with more plagioclase feldspar crystals

Aplite dike: a dike of small $\frac{1}{32}$ to $\frac{1}{8}$ inch (a few mm) grains of quartz and feldspar and lacking dark minerals

Bajada: a broad, gently sloping surface of rock debris formed by lateral coalescence of fans at the base of a desert mountain

Basalt: fine-grained, dark-colored volcanic rock rich in magnesium and iron

Caliche: a sediment or soil layer cemented by calcium carbonate; common in arid regions

Conjugate joints: two sets of joints that intersect at angles of 60 and 120 degrees

Dike: a sheetlike igneous intrusion that cuts across the grain of the rock into which it has intruded

Erosion: the wearing down and transportation of rock materials of the earth's surface

Extrusive: the general term for igneous rocks that erupt and form volcanic features on the earth's surface

Fault: a fracture in the earth's crust along which there has been displacement

Gneiss: a common metamorphic rock, often of the same composition as granitic rocks, but in which the mineral grains are aligned in distinct bands called foliation

Granite: a common coarse-grained, light-colored intrusive (plutonic) igneous rock composed primarily of feldspar and quartz

Igneous rocks: rocks that have crystallized from molten material within the earth (plutonic) or at the surface of the earth (volcanic)

Inselberg: isolated, steep-walled residual bedrock knob that stands above a pediment

Intrusive: a general term for coarse-grained plutonic igneous rocks that have cooled slowly beneath the earth's surface

Joint: separation or parting in a rock that has not been displaced

Lateral-slip fault: a fault along which movement has been horizontal

Lithosphere: the solid outer layer of the earth, consisting of the crust and upper mantle.

Lithospheric plates: large, curved, rigid but mobile slabs of the earth's crust and upper mantle on the order of 60 miles (100 km) thick that move relative to one another. The interaction between plates causes much geologic activity in the crust.

Magma: the parent molten material from which igneous rocks form

Marine: the general term for rocks that accumulate in an oceanic environment

Megacrysts (phenocrysts): large crystals, up to a few inches or centimeters, commonly feldspar, that are enmeshed in a finer-grained igneous rock

Metamorphic rock: rock that has been altered from a pre-existing rock by heat, pressure, or chemically active fluids

Monzogranite: a light-colored variety of granite containing approximately equal amounts of alkali (potassium and sodium) feldspar and plagioclase feldspar

Mylonite: a variety of gneiss that has formed in a fault zone

Offset: amount of displacement across opposite sides of a fault

Pangaea: a supercontinent that grew in late Paleozoic times, but then split apart during the Mesozoic. The Atlantic Ocean formed as Pangaea broke up.

Pediment: planar, gently sloping, rock-cut bedrock surface that is carved at the base of a desert mountain, commonly merging with a bajada at its lower end

Pegmatite dike: a dike consisting of very large crystals, up to a few inches across, composed primarily of quartz and feldspar and usually some mica minerals

Plate tectonics: the theory that the earth's surface is composed of rigid but mobile lithospheric plates that move and interact with one another

Pluton: any body of igneous rock that forms by molten igneous material rising into the shallow crust and cools and hardens without erupting at the earth's surface

Rock varnish: thin, dark, iron- and magnesium-rich material that coats many rock surfaces

Rodinia: a Proterozoic supercontinent that eventually separated to become North America, Antarctica, and Australia

Sandstone: a common sedimentary rock composed primarily of sand grains that have been cemented together by trace amounts of silica or calcite

Sedimentary rock: layered rock commonly formed from the cementing together of loose sediment desposited in water, or from biological and chemical activity in the water

Subduction: the sinking of one lithospheric plate beneath another at a convergent plate margin

Tafoni: a honeycomb structure of pits and hollows initiated by subsoil chemical weathering

Terrane: a rock or group of rocks and the area in which they crop out

Tonalite: a variety of granite lacking significant alkali feldspar

Vein: a thin, crosscutting, sheetlike intrusion, usually composed of quartz

Ventifact: rock that has been sculpted by wind

Weathering: the chemical and physical breakdown of rock materials by interaction with the atmosphere and biosphere

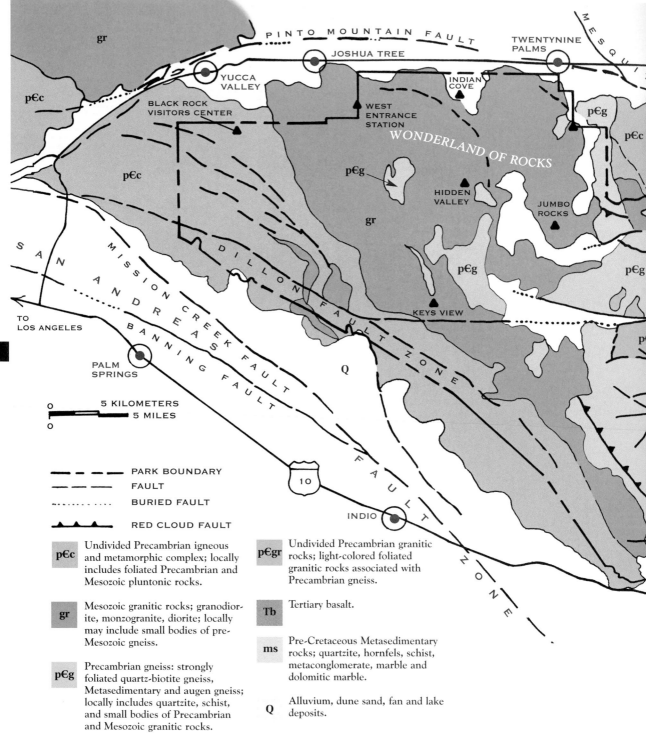

PARK BOUNDARY
FAULT
BURIED FAULT
RED CLOUD FAULT

p€c Undivided Precambrian igneous and metamorphic complex; locally includes foliated Precambrian and Mesozoic pluntonic rocks.

gr Mesozoic granitic rocks; granodiorite, monzogranite, diorite; locally may include small bodies of pre-Mesozoic gneiss.

p€g Precambrian gneiss: strongly foliated quartz-biotite gneiss, Metasedimentary and augen gneiss; locally includes quartzite, schist, and small bodies of Precambrian and Mesozoic granitic rocks.

p€gr Undivided Precambrian granitic rocks; light-colored foliated granitic rocks associated with Precambrian gneiss.

Tb Tertiary basalt.

ms Pre-Cretaceous Metasedimentary rocks; quartzite, hornfels, schist, metaconglomerate, marble and dolomitic marble.

Q Alluvium, dune sand, fan and lake deposits.

Geology from Bishop, 1963; Bortungo and Spittler, 1986; Jennings, 1967; Rogers, 1965.

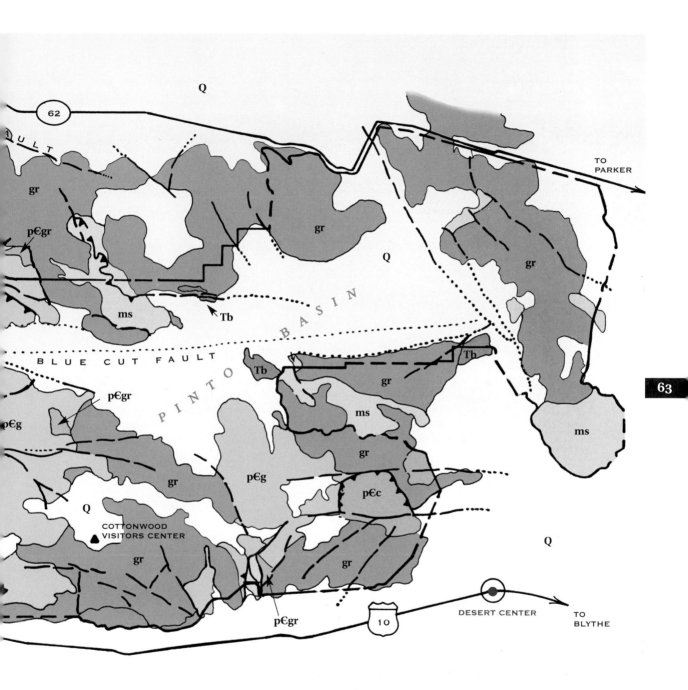

Geologic Map of Joshua Tree National Park

ACKNOWLEDGMENTS

Many thanks for the suggestion and encouragement to write this book are due to Joe Zarki, Chief of Interpretation at Joshua Tree National Park. Thanks, too, for encouragement and patience, especially with missed deadlines, go to Ken Tinquist, former Executive Director of the Joshua Tree National Park Association, and to his successor, Nancy Downer. Valuable thoughts, perceptive questions and sharp-witted ideas were contributed by Darwin Spearing and Elizabeth VanZandt, both of whom are ranger naturalists at the park and delightful companions in the field. Thanks to Byron Kesler of Volcano, Hawaii, for taking our rough scratchings and converting them into a geologic map. Special thanks are due to William B. Bull, of the University of Arizona, J. Lawford Anderson of the University of Southern California, Andrew Barth of Indiana University, Howard G. Wilshire and Jane Nielson of the U.S. Geological Survey, Robert Reynolds of LSA Associates, Inc., Forrest Hopson, independent geologist, Reno, Nevada, and George W. Bergantz of the University of Washington, all of whom contributed significant ideas critical to the improvement of our effort. We especially wish to thank Christina Watkins and Sandra Scott for their keen eye to layout, detail and accuracy; and to Susan Leach who massaged our sketches into works of art. No less appreciated are several generations of geology students who for more than 30 years have observed, thought, and asked questions about the geology of the park that helped shape our perceptions and understanding while forcing us to fine tune our thinking and our explanations. Any errors of omission or commission, of course, are our responsibility.

D.D. Trent,
Glendora, California
R.W. Hazlett
Claremont, California

ABOUT THE AUTHORS

D.D. "Dee" Trent received his undergraduate degree in geology from the University of Southern California and his Ph.D. from the University of Arizona. For several years he was employed as a geologist in the oil industry, his work taking him to California's San Joaquin Valley, Utah, Arizona, and Alaska. For 28 years he taught geology, and oceanography at Citrus College, Glendora, California, and is now retired. He is co-author of a widely-used college textbook, *Geology and the Environment,* makes several cameo appearances in the PBS telecourse series, *The Earth Revealed,* and is a frequent lecturer on cruise ships. Dr. Trent and his wife reside in Claremont, California.

Richard Hazlett received degrees in geology from Occidental College, Dartmouth, and the University of Southern California, specializing in the study of volcanoes, both active and extinct. His research includes having done geologicial mapping which helped establish the Turtle Mountain Wilderness in the eastern Mojave Desert. Other studies have taken him to Alaska, Hawaii, Italy, and Central America. Dr. Hazlett is co-author of *Roadside Geology of Hawaii,* and currently teaches geology and environmental studies at Pomona College in Claremont, California.